An illustrated guide to

THE DORSET AND EAST DEVON COAST

JOHN CHAFFEY

**DORSET
BOOKS**

First published in Great Britain in 2003

Copyright © 2003 John Chaffey

Frontispiece photograph: *Seaton Bay*

Dedicated to Ruth, my constant walking companion.

British Library Cataloguing-in-Publication Data
A CIP record for this title is available from the British Library

ISBN 1 871164 56 7

DORSET BOOKS
Official publisher to Dorset County Council

Halsgrove House
Lower Moor Way
Tiverton, Devon EX16 6SS
Tel: 01884 243242
Fax: 01884 243325
email: sales@halsgrove.com
website: www.halsgrove.com

Printed and bound by D'Auria Industrie Grafiche Spa, Italy

CONTENTS

ACKNOWLEDGEMENTS

My thanks are due to John Newth, Managing Director of *Dorset Life, The Dorset Magazine,* who first encouraged me to write a series of articles on the Dorset coast for the magazine, and which are now included in this book. My colleagues in the Dorset Geologists' Association, with whom I have spent much time on the Dorset and East Devon coast, have helped me towards a fuller understanding of the magnificent geology of the World Heritage Site. Finally, as always, my thanks go to my wife, Ruth. Her support and encouragement have been unfailing.

SELECTED READING

Allison, Robert J., (Ed), *The Coastal Landforms of West Dorset Geologists' Association Guide,* No.47, 1992.

Bird, Eric, *The Geology and Scenery of Dorset,* Ex Libris Press, 1995.

Bird, Eric and Modlock, Lilian, *Writers on the South West Coast,* Ex Libris Press, 1994.★

Dorset Geologists' Association Group, *Coast and Country, Geology Walks in and around Dorset* (in press).

Durrance, E.M. and Laming, D.J.C (Ed), *The Geology of Devon,* University of Exeter Press, 1982.

House, Michael, *Geology of the Dorset Coast,* Geologists' Association Guide, 1989.

Legg, Rodney, *The Jurassic Coast,* Dorset Publishing Company, 2002.

★ The origin of all quotes used in this book can be found in *Writers on the South West Coast* (above).

1
THE WORLD HERITAGE SITE

After over five years of intensive preparation, the nomination of the Dorset and East Devon Coast as a World Heritage Site was submitted to UNESCO in July 2000. An assessment visit was carried out on behalf of UNESCO in February 2001. Dr Paul Dingwall, a senior conservationist from New Zealand, spent five days examining the coast and its management. He found a 'compelling' case for designation and all of his comments were both positive and encouraging. The Dorset and East Devon Coast was finally designated in December 2001, when it was inscribed on the list of World Heritage Sites. It is the only natural World Heritage Site in England and now has the same status as the Giant's Causeway and St Kilda in the United Kingdom, and such world-famous examples as the Grand Canyon and the Great Barrier Reef.

The nomination was made because it was felt that the Dorset and East Devon Coast met two UNESCO criteria essential to the designation of World Heritage Sites:

Firstly that the site should be an outstanding example, representing major stages of the earth's history including the record of life, significant ongoing geological processes in the development of landforms, or significant geomorphic or physiographic features; and secondly that the site should contain superlative natural phenomena or areas of exceptional natural beauty and aesthetic importance.

How does the Dorset and East Devon Coast measure up to these demanding criteria? The coast displays a remarkable geological sequence spanning about 185 million years, including the Triassic, Jurassic and Cretaceous Periods of geological time. The rocks of the coast are exposed in a series of magnificent cliff sections from Orcombe Point, near Exmouth, in the west to South Beach, Studland, in the Isle of Purbeck in the east. The oldest Triassic rocks are exposed at Orcombe Rocks, and since the dip of the beds is to the east, most parts of the geological succession are visible and generally accessible in sequence up to the Cretaceous beds which outcrop most prominently on the Purbeck coast.

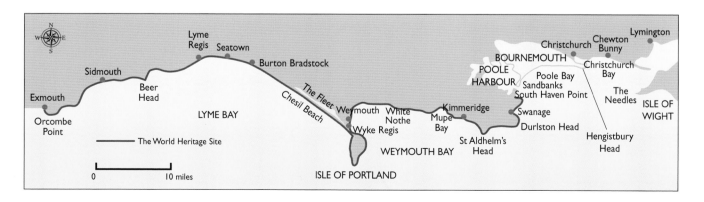

The Triassic rocks, exposed in the cliffs of the East Devon part of the nominated site, offer an almost complete sequence of red beds, laid down for the most part in ancient desert-like conditions, apart from the uppermost sequence, which was deposited in relatively shallow seas. To the east the Jurassic rocks, which outcrop in the cliffs from Lyme Regis in the west to the western and southern parts of the Isle of Purbeck in the east, display one of the outstanding sequences of rocks of this age anywhere in the world. They have been intensively studied since the early days of geology as a science (the late-eighteenth and early-nineteenth century) when many of the leading geologists, including William Buckland, William Conybeare and Sir Henry de la Beche visited and worked on the Dorset coast. Today, the Jurassic sequence is of international importance and provides a series of classic type-sections with which most contemporary studies elsewhere are compared. All stages of the Cretaceous Period (except the uppermost) are included in the succession within the nominated site.

The nominated site includes a wide range of fossil localities of international importance. Between Lyme Regis and Seatown, the Lower Jurassic rocks represent a particularly important locality for marine fossils such as ammonites, belemnites, bivalves and crinoids and is an outstanding location for fossil reptiles. In the east the Purbeckian strata display one of the most outstanding terrestrial sequences anywhere in the world and have yielded a particularly rich fauna of dinosaur and other vertebrate remains, together with invertebrates and fossil plants. At a number of other important sites, discovered fossil assemblages have made fundamental contributions to the science of palaeontology.

The Dorset and East Devon Coast has become increasingly important for the study of geological processes and coastal development. Over 200,000 pupils and students are involved in educational visits to the Dorset coast each year. The area between Lyme Regis and Bridport is a classic area for the study of landslips and the effect they have on human coastal settlements. Chesil Beach, extending 18 miles from West Bay to Chiswell on the Isle of Portland, is a unique shingle structure yet to be explained convincingly. Portland's limestone block, with its characteristic landslips, is itself one of most distinctive structural features on the entire coast of Britain. The coast of Purbeck and Lulworth illustrates a variety of erosional landforms without parallel elsewhere and has long been regarded as the basic model in most standard textbooks.

Chesil Beach from West Weare

The nominated site has an unchallenged aesthetic quality, which has long inspired writers, artists and composers. Thomas Hardy set important sequences of his novels on the Dorset coast and locations such as the Isle of Slingers and Knollsea, Budmouth and Port Bredy find a ready echo along the coast today. The widely varying sequence of rocks along the coast contributes much to its immediate scenic attraction; few contrasts can be greater than that of the magnificent red cliffs and stacks of Ladram Bay with the great bastion of White Nothe overlooking Weymouth Bay, or of the menacing splendour of Black Ven with the intimate charm of Osmington Mills or Church Ope Cove on Portland. The unlimited horizons of Lyme Bay, the infinite cliff-and-bay variety of Lulworth's coast and the sturdy lime-stone ramparts of Purbeck's southern cliffs all illustrate the coast's stunning character and enduring appeal.

With such a range of natural assets, the precious heritage of the Dorset and East Devon Coast needs adequate protection in the form of conservation management and planning controls. Most of the site lies within two Areas of Outstanding Natural Beauty: the East Devon AONB and the Dorset AONB. Further protection is provided by the three Heritage Coasts defined within East Devon and Dorset. Conservation interests are served through the designation of National Nature Reserves, Sites of Special Scientific Interest, Special Protection Areas, Special Marine Conservation Areas and Ramsar Wetland Sites. The Dorset Coast Forum, which draws together over 100 different organisations and interests, has promoted the nomination for World Heritage status most strongly from the beginning.

The nomination considered the Dorset and East Devon Coast to be, in the words of UNESCO, 'of outstanding universal value'. Designation as a World Heritage Site will bring many benefits to the coast. It will command interna-tional respect for the conservation of a globally important coastline. Opportunities for developing the coast as an

Golden Cap from near St Gabriel's Mouth

Burton Cliff, near Burton Bradstock

educational resource of international repute will include the establishment of major centres dedicated to the interpretation of its geology and landscape, and the continued maintenance of a vigorous programme of newly funded scientific research. Important fossil specimens will be increasingly available for public display and scientific study. Positive restructuring of the tourist industry will highlight opportunities for sustainable specialist interest and educational holidays.

Nevertheless, some reservations have been expressed over the designation; there is concern that it might lead to an even greater influx of visitors than that which already exists in the summer. Received wisdom is that this is unlikely to be the case, particularly if greater use is made of the 'shoulder' months for special-interest groups. Another worry is that World Heritage status would bring in its wake a plethora of new planning regulations. However, the raft of present controls is already a highly effective one, and designation would impose no additional constraints nor have any other implications for the planning system.

Although the World Heritage Site officially ends at South Beach, Studland, it was felt appropriate to include the remainder of the Dorset coast, from Poole Harbour to Chewton Bunny, in this book. The harbours of Poole and Christchurch are two of the finest estuarine environments on the south coast of England. Both are much-valued coastal landscapes and possess remarkable diversity of wildlife and their high conservation status is properly recognised. Lying between these two beautiful stretches of water, forming a remarkable contrast, is Dorset's urban coastline, which runs from Sandbanks to just west of Hengistbury Head. Here, in the short space of two hundred years, empty sandy beaches and lonely pine-clad cliff tops have seen the rise of one of Britain's outstanding resorts, with its magnificent backdrop of the Isle of Purbeck and the Isle of Wight, separated by the sparkling waters of Poole Bay.

The Pinnacles, south of Old Harry Rocks

2
ORCOMBE POINT TO SIDMOUTH

The World Heritage Coast begins just to the east of Exmouth, at Orcombe Point, where the red Triassic rocks form a low headland just beyond the eastern fringe of the seaside town. Eastwards from Orcombe the coast tends to grow in stature and interest towards Sidmouth.

It is a coastline that reflects its rich Devon hinterland of sweeping hills, red soils and wooded ridges. Relatively low red sandstone cliffs are a dominant theme as far as Ladram Bay, but the stretch between Ladram and Sidmouth takes on a much more dramatic nature, with the cliffs soaring to the wooded heights of High Peak, and continuing in unbroken red splendour to Sidmouth itself. To many this stretch of coastline is the essence of seaside Devon, part recreation and

High Peak and sea stacks near Ladram Bay

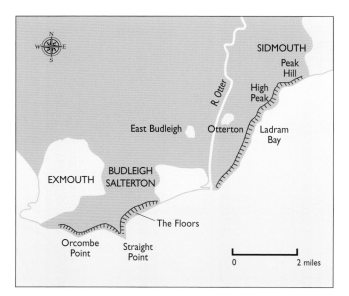

leisure, part retirement, set against a backdrop of splendid rich and fertile Devon countryside. Unlike much of the Heritage Coast to the east no villages break the rural sweep of red-soiled fields between the resorts of Exmouth and Sidmouth; only the discreet charm of Budleigh Salterton, with its modest promenade and pebbly beach adds a note of quiet urban style to the centre of this coast.

Geology has ensured that this stretch of coastline has its own modest but distinctive physical presence. With the exception of the Cretaceous rocks that cap both High Peak and Peak Hill to the west of Sidmouth, the rocks that form this section of the East Devon coast are all of Triassic age, and are almost uniformly red to reddish-brown in colour. Their colour is an indication of their desert origin; thin coatings of iron oxide on the grains of sand within the sandstones are responsible for the red colouration and readily recall the

Orcombe Point

Cliffs at Budleigh Salterton

Mouth of the River Otter

great sweep of red dunes and sheets of gravel in the African, Arabian and Asiatic deserts of today. So, in Triassic times, East Devon was part of a huge desert landscape that occupied much of the southern part of present-day Devon. From time to time great floods swept across the flat desert plains, bringing in vast quantities of sand, gravel and pebbles. Temporary lakes on the desert surface allowed the accumulation of much finer sediments.

At Orcombe Point desert sandstones form the reefs that fringe the low cliffs. Further east, finer mudstones give way to the spectacular Budleigh Salterton Pebble Beds that first appear in the cliffs at West Down Beacon, and gradually descend eastwards to reach beach level just west of Budleigh itself. These Pebble Beds were laid down in a large, north-flowing river that rushed across the desert plain. Beyond Budleigh Salterton the Otter Sandstone, that forms the cliffs as far as the eastern side of Ladram Bay, is mostly river-laid sand. The Triassic succession is completed by the finer-grained Mercia Mudstones that first appear in the upper levels of the cliffs just to the west of High Peak, and then gradually descend to lower levels eastwards towards Sidmouth.

Marine erosion has carved a series of relatively modest cliffs as far east as Ladram Bay. In places, such as The Floors to the east of West Down Farm, landslipping within the mudstones gives a much more tumbled appearance to the cliffs. However, between Otterton Ledge, just beyond the spit half-enclosing the mouth of the Otter, and Ladram Bay, relatively uniform cliffs edged by pebble beaches or sandstone reefs form a seaward fringe to the gently rolling fields that run southwards from Otterton. Almost without warning, the coastal character changes at Ladram Bay. Here a magnificent series of towering stacks have been cut in the Otter Sandstone, reminiscent perhaps of the great sea stacks that can be seen at the red sandstone coasts of Caithness or Orkney. Vertical joints within the rock have controlled the precipitous nature of the stacks, and near-horizontal bedding planes separating successive beds of sandstone have influenced the form of the platforms and reefs that run out from the foot of the cliffs. The commanding heights of High Peak, less easy of access since afforestation blurred their outline over the past thirty years or so, bring the first hint of the great cliff sequences that dominate so much of the Heritage Coast to the east. Here, and on Peak Hill to the east, the most westerly outcrops of Cretaceous Upper Greensand form a capping to the Triassic rocks reflecting once again the inner Devon landscape, with its wooded Greensand crests looming above the red fields of the East Devon valleys.

Sidmouth's narrow beach breaks the continuity of the now-established Greensand-capped Mercia Mudstone cliffs that continue almost without a break to Branscombe. Vaughan Cornish, the local geographer, described the Sidmouth scene to perfection when he wrote, 'The red cliffs of Sidmouth do so much to redeem the dullness of the English winter that

Windgate and Sidmouth

they do provide some compensation for the sunshine of the Mediterranean shore.'

The human scene on this stretch of the Heritage Coast focuses principally on three resorts. In 1750 Dr Richard Pococke wrote of Exmouth, just to the west of the Heritage Site, 'The situation is so pleasant, having beautiful little hills to the east finely improved, and a view of the fine country on the other side, that persons of condition have come to live in the place.' This eighteenth-century view of Exmouth still rings true, although the 'persons of condition' are now mostly retired and they have been joined by the many commuters that now work in nearby Exeter. Its fine Georgian buildings possess real architectural merit, and history records that Lady Nelson and Lady Byron both had homes in the town.

Between Exmouth and Budleigh Salterton, a huge caravan complex spreads across the cliff top behind Straight Point, in strange juxtaposition with the firing range on the headland itself. Apart from the smaller development at Ladram Bay, this coastline has largely been spared this type of development. Budleigh Salterton, nestling in the shadow of West Down, and overlooking the marshy, part-drained stretches of the lower Otter valley, does not have the urbane attractions of Exmouth, but is still essentially retirement Devon. It is likely to be known through Sir John Millais' painting 'The Boyhood of Raleigh', set on the beach at Budleigh. The sea wall in the painting is still retained on the waterfront and Millais' house still stands in the town.

Beyond High Peak and Peak Hill, Sidmouth has spread from 'the little fisher town' at the mouth of the Sid over the rolling fields of the immediate hinterland; the tide of retirement bungalows has engulfed the upstream village of Sidford. The town began to prosper in Napoleonic times, when travel for the wealthy in Europe was much curtailed – an early-nineteenth century guide claimed:

… as a watering place it is now much frequented, the company every season generally amounting to three hundred! [sic]. The inhabitants are remarkable for their healthy appearance and their longevity. Such indeed, might be naturally expected, from the suitability of the air, the fine dry soil, and a situation the most delicious, open to the oceans, yet not subject to fogs, and screened from all but the southern winds.

However, its situation has meant that it is also exposed to southerly storms, and the great storm of 1824 that wrought such destruction further east along the coast at Lyme Regis and Chiswell on Portland, caused severe damage in the town. Coastal defence at Sidmouth is still an important theme in the work of East Devon's civil engineers.

The westernmost stretch of the World Heritage Coast is thus essentially red Devon at the seaside. Seen from the summit of High Peak to the west of Sidmouth, its cliffed coastline has an immediate and lasting appeal. Looking west the low cliffs beyond Ladram are framed by the placid waters of the Exe estuary and the brooding slopes of far-off Dartmoor rising beyond the wooded Haldon Hills. Looking eastwards the red cliffs stretch beyond Sidmouth towards Branscombe. Distant Hooken and Beer Head are the first Chalk headlands and precursors to the magnificent Chalk scenery found further along the coast in Dorset.

3
SIDMOUTH TO LYME REGIS

The stretch of coastline that lies between Sidmouth and Lyme Regis is outstanding. Eastwards from Sidmouth, Devon's red Triassic rocks still add their distinctive colour to the cliffs, but beyond Branscombe the cliff landscape of Hooken marks a dramatic change. Two of the dominant characteristics of much of the Heritage Coast make their appearance here. Under Hooken, with its great inaccessible pinnacles of slipped rock, is the first large-scale landslip complex to be encountered on an eastwards traverse of the coast. Chalk also makes its first appearance to the east of Branscombe, and Beer Head, with its brilliant white cliffs, forms a landmark easily distinguished from far to the east in Dorset. Beyond Seaton's unpretentious seaside appeal, and the Axe's attractive estuary, the great landslips from Bindon to the western outskirts of Lyme Regis dominate the coastal scene. In some respects this National Nature Reserve is the Heritage Coast's most closely guarded secret. Although traversed by the South West Coast Path, much of the thickly vegetated landscape of foundered cliff and ill-balanced rock

masses is barely accessible. Lyme Regis, at its eastern end, itself threatened by landslips, is West Dorset's seaside gem. Few of the Heritage Coast's towns can offer such a splendid landscape setting, a geological environment so rich, or so distinguished a seaside history.

Geologically speaking, this stretch of coastline sees the transition between red Devon and Jurassic Dorset. The Mercia Mudstones, which made their first appearance in the cliffs of High Peak to the west of Sidmouth, prevail in the coastal profile as far east as Branscombe, and then reappear at Seaton Hole, where they are brought up into the cliff face once again by a huge fault or fracture in the earth's crust. They reappear briefly in the cliffs in the western part of the Axmouth to Lyme Undercliff, and then gently slip beneath sea level as they dip eastwards beyond Bindon. The very youngest Triassic rocks, the so-called Penarth Group, shales and mudstones, appear briefly in the Undercliff. East of Branscombe, it is rocks of Cretaceous age, overlying the

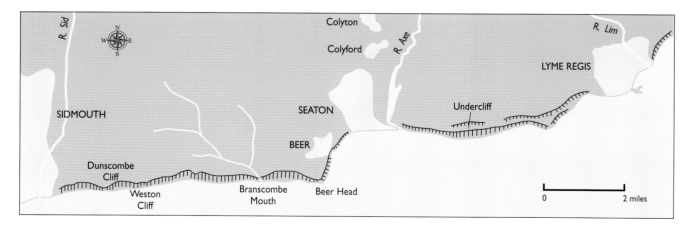

Sidmouth and the coast to the east

Under Hooken, from Beer Head

red Triassic, that add so much to the character of the coastline. Cretaceous Upper Greensand first appeared as a capping to the cliffs at High Peak and Peak Hill to the west of Sidmouth, but east of this town this yellowish-brown rock occupies progressively more of the cliff towards Branscombe, although it has little effect on the overall profile of the cliff. Chalk, of the Upper Cretaceous Period, makes its first appearance in the upper part of the cliff at Dunscombe to the east of Sidmouth, and gradually dips eastwards so that at Beer Head it reaches sea level, and occupies the full height of the cliff. Beer is more of a Chalk-cliff town than any in Dorset, and only Freshwater on the Isle of Wight or Seaford in distant Sussex can lay claim to being embraced by the Chalk in the same way.

The geology of the Axmouth to Lyme Undercliff is both complicated and obscured by landslips. In the west, to the east of Axmouth, the Triassic rocks crop out at the base of the cliffs, with the Upper Greensand and Chalk forming the upper levels of the cliff. Further eastwards the oldest Jurassic rocks, the Blue Lias, so familiar in the cliffs of Lyme Regis, occur in the lower levels of the cliffs at the Bindon landslide, although the Upper Greensand and Chalk persist in the much-slipped upper levels.

Eastwards from Sidmouth the cliffed coast to Branscombe is very much a reflection of the inland landscape. At the coast the Greensand plateau of the hinterland reaches the sea, and erosion has produced a series of remarkably uniform cliffs, broken by the combes cut by the short streams that drain down from Salcombe Regis and Weston to the east. Inland from Branscombe Mouth a whole network of streams has cut deeply into the Upper Greensand to expose the red Mercia Mudstones in their valleys – a last glimpse of red Devon, forming an attractive backdrop to the well-used beach where the main stream trickles into the sea.

The Hooken landslip, with its undercliff of detached masses of rock, such as the great columns of the Pinnacles, owes its existence to the juxtaposition of rocks of varying permeability. Water percolates down through the permeable Chalk and the Upper Greensand in the higher levels of the cliff, and then encounters an impermeable layer, where it emerges, causing instability in the whole rock sequence. A well-documented event was the great slip of March 1790. In the preceding year, a huge crack opened up in South Down Common cutting off about ten acres of land on the cliff top. This huge slice slipped downwards some 250ft a year later, creating the undercliff of Upper Greensand capped by columns of Chalk in the Pinnacles. High in the Chalk cliffs behind, exposed by the 1790 slip, can be seen an adit, indicating where the famous Beer Stone was worked within the Chalk. Similar instability has been responsible for the recent slip at Seaton Hole, which has necessitated the building of a new path to give access to the beach there.

East of the mouth of the Axe lies one of the most celebrated landslip complexes in Britain. Although the whole of this 5-mile stretch is affected by landslips, the most famous and probably the best documented is the event that occurred at Bindon in 1839. Both William Conybeare and William Buckland, early and influential geologists, were in the area at the time and together wrote a report – the first real scientific analysis of a major landslip. They correctly identified the role of downward percolating water in causing 'the lower region of the foxmould (the lowest layers of the Upper Greensand)... [to become] so highly saturated with water as to reduce to semifluid quicksand.' The liquefaction of these layers caused the sliding and foundering of the great mass of Upper Greensand and overlying Chalk. Buckland wrote:

Fifty acres were gradually severed from the mainland during 26 December. Of these a portion subsided about fifty feet below its former level, and the rest sank into a chasm extending three quarters of a mile from east to west and varying in breadth from 200 to 400 feet.

Hooken Landslip, the Pinnacles and the coast looking west to Sidmouth and beyond.

Two coastguards witnessed these events at close quarters, and fled across fields riven with fresh deep cracks; they probably considered themselves lucky to escape with their lives. Much of the still-unstable landslipped area is now covered with fine ash woods, whose luxuriance can be explored along the coastal footpath, although the green half-light of the route is unrelieved by any views of either cliff or sea.

Apart from Beer and Seaton, human settlement has largely shunned this often-unstable coast; farms and villages have been built on sites on the Greensand and Chalk plateaux farther inland. Unspoilt Beer is a sheer delight. It nestles in

Seaton Hole

The Beach at Beer

its deep valley, with the small, clear Beer stream running in a stone channel along the main street. The valley opens onto a sheltered, flint-pebble beach, which is reminiscent of a seaside scene that is now all but lost elsewhere. Here brightly painted fishing boats are drawn up in haphazard fashion, seafood stalls and deck-chair stands are linked to the main street by matting pathways to cushion unaccustomed feet against the crunching pebbles, and footpaths meander lazily up to the heights of Annis' Knob that overlook the beach.

Seaton grew on the sheltered western side of the mouth of the Axe valley. As the railway made its way into the South West, tiny branch lines slipped down towards the sea from little stations, such as Seaton Junction and Sidmouth Junction, now lost in railway history. With the railway came the Victorian and Edwardian visitors ready to enjoy the delights of the pebble beach, the enticing sea water and the fine views out to the stunning white headland beyond Beer. In August 1871 the Revd Francis Kilvert found that 'the beach was thronged, swarming, a gay merry scene, light dresses, parasols, straw hats… I never saw the sea more intensely, wonderfully blue.'

The eastern half of the East Devon section of the Heritage Coast offers a contrasting mix of impressive, lonely and often remote landslipped cliffs, while its two seaside settlements, Beer and Seaton, have their own atmospheres of village and resort appeal respectively. Beer Head, and the Chalk cliffs which enfold Beer itself suggest affinities with the great sweep of Chalk from White Nothe to Worbarrow Bay in Dorset. Seaton's western cliffs and the cliffs of Dunscombe and Weston are still very much red Devon. Beer and Seaton have an unmistakable Devon ambience, but away to the east, beyond this coast where the threads of culture and landscape of the two counties are interwoven, stands Dorset's gloriously scenic frontier town, Lyme Regis.

4
LYME REGIS TO SEATOWN

After having driven along the somewhat featureless road from Colyford in Devon to Lyme Regis, the first glimpses of the Dorset coast through the trees in Lyme's leafy western outskirts always create a frisson of anticipation and excitement. The soaring heights of Black Ven, Stonebarrow Hill and Golden Cap dominate the half-hidden view, but one is soon aware of their full majestic sweep, when seen from the ancient Cobb sheltering the harbour at Lyme Regis. Few landscape contrasts are as remarkable as that between the orange-yellow capping of these coastal bastions of West Dorset and the sombre greys and blacks of their tumbled, and often chaotic lower slopes. It is this very confusion in these slopes that carries a slight hint of menace and uncertainty too, for this is a coast dominated by landslips, on a scale unparalleled in the whole of Europe. Much of the lower part of Lyme Regis is itself built on an ancient landslip, still very far from being completely stable, and the cliffs as far east as Seatown all bear witness to the frequent, slipped, changes in their profile. The stunning beauty of this coast can be enjoyed in different moods in the changing seasons. High summer sees the sun highlighting the bright summits of the cliffs, often fading away to a haze towards the distant Bridport cliffs and the long sweep of Chesil Bank. Winter gales bring great seas in from the Channel, combing down the beach gravels and washing away the fresh debris from new landslips at the base of the dark cliffs that are seamed with countless small runnels, the waters of which are stained grey with the fine particles eroded from the unstable slips. It is in the heart of winter that dark storm clouds, racing across the

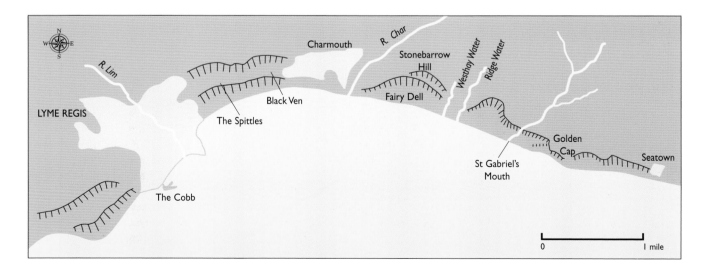

Lyme Regis Harbour and the Cobb

East Cliff, Lyme Regis and Black Ven

The Spittles to the east of Lyme Regis, with its landslips

hidden summits of the cliffs, emphasise the essential wild nature of this desolate coast, accessible only at the mouth of the little River Char, with its constantly changing, gravel-encumbered exit to the sea.

Geology has exerted a remarkable control on the development of the landscape and scenery of this western section of Dorset's coastline. The cliffs are made up of rocks that date from the Lower Jurassic Period (they are approximately 180–200 million years old) capped by rocks from the Cretaceous age (Upper Greensand approximately 100 million years old). It was in the former rocks that Mary Anning first discovered the remains of Jurassic reptiles in the early-nineteenth century and established the area's reputation for fossils that it retains nearly two hundred years later.

The Upper Greensand rocks that cap the cliffs of West Dorset are permeable – in other words they readily allow water to pass through. By way of contrast the rocks below are impermeable and prevent the downward movement of water. This leads to the rocks immediately underlying the Upper Greensand becoming unstable; they are no longer able to support the weight of the rocks above, causing the collapse of the overlying Greensand in huge slips. Probably the most dramatic of these slips occurred over the border in neighbouring Devon at Christmas 1839, when 50 acres of land became separated from the area inland by a chasm over 200ft deep. Although none of the slips in West Dorset have achieved these proportions, the whole of the upper faces of Black Ven, Stonebarrow Hill and to a lesser extent Golden Cap are scarred by landslips. The slips on Black Ven have affected part of the golf course immediately inland and have resulted in the diversion of the South West Coast Path along this stretch. On Stonebarrow Hill the old radar station was displaced by a huge slip in 1942.

Below the upper parts of the cliffs on Black Ven the surfaces of the Lower Jurassic rocks are very unstable and dangerous.

The instability manifests itself in great mudslides that run down to the water's edge at the base of the cliff and form huge lobes running out over the foreshore. These are gradually eroded by the sea to leave a series of boulder arcs to mark the former extent of the lobes. On Stonebarrow the pattern is slightly different; a huge amphitheatre, known as Fairy Dell, occupies the zone immediately downwards from the upper cliffs. This hollow is much affected by slips and mudslides, which deliver debris to the beach over the steep cliffs on the seaward side. Golden Cap, at 627ft the highest point on the south coast of England, has its own very distinctive profile. Unlike Black Ven and Stonebarrow Hill it is a true promontory, projecting seawards from the general run of the coast. It owes its flat top to a capping of Upper Greensand. Its cliffs are steeper than those to the west, a reflection of different geology and more active erosion at its base. This is part of the West Dorset Heritage Coast, and its landscape and scenic qualities inevitably attract large numbers of tourists; nearly half a million holiday-makers each year, together with two million day visitors.

Stonebarrow Cliffs, east of Charmouth

Concentration of accommodation is particularly heavy in the Charmouth area, with over 5000 bed spaces available, the majority of which are in caravan parks. Both Lyme Regis and Seatown offer roughly half that number of bed spaces.

Coastal defence is another important issue in the three settlements on this stretch of coast. Not only is erosion a problem that has to be addressed, but landslipping also demands attention. Lyme Regis has embarked on its ambitious five-phase Environmental Improvements Scheme, which embraces sewage treatment, coastal defence, heritage protection on the Cobb, and amenity provision. Charmouth has a coastal defence scheme which protects the Heritage Centre and the visitors' car park. The hamlet of Seatown suffers from landslipping, which has been threatening both the Anchor Inn and residential properties and it is hoped that recent work carried out here should provide added protection. Success in coastal defence policies can only be judged in the long term; the coastal settlements of the far west of Dorset must await the judgement of time. On such a high quality coast, it is increasingly important that coastal managers are seen to be working with nature, rather than against it. Despite the difficulties, it is a principle that future policies should try to embrace.

Seatown and Golden Cap

Notwithstanding the current problems of tourist pressure and coastal defence management, the appeal of this coast is an enduring one. Within a relatively short distance, the bright coastal waterfalls of Westhay and Ridge Waters contrast with the threatening, ever-shifting slips at the Spittles, and the remote St Gabriel's Mouth seems far from the busy beaches of Charmouth and Lyme Regis. Golden Cap will continue to dominate a scene of constantly changing cliffs, and daily renewed sand and gravel beaches, rich assets in West Dorset's landscape heritage.

5
SEATOWN TO BURTON BRADSTOCK

Although perhaps not quite so dramatic as the stretch of coast to the west, the cliffs and valleys of the coast between Seatown and Burton Bradstock have their own very distinctive appeal. Seen from the promenade at West Bay, the cliffs to the west surge in a series of broken curves to the commanding heights of Thorncombe Beacon, and then descend more gently to the well-marked profile of Doghouse Hill. Eastwards from West Bay's harbour entrance a view unfolds of the unmistakable golden sandstones that make up the serrated East Cliff, and beyond Burton

Freshwater, the more distant Burton Cliff. Landslips still remain a menace along this stretch of coast, although they are most serious at West Bay itself. To the west, the lower slopes of West Cliff, Thorncombe Beacon and Doghouse Hill all bear witness to similar instability. To the east the profiles of the near-vertical cliffs that confront the sea as far as Burton Bradstock are unbroken by landslipping. Along this stretch, the huge piles of rock debris at the base of the exposed cliffs suggest rates of erosion that are a concern for all those who own land adjacent to the coastline. Here too,

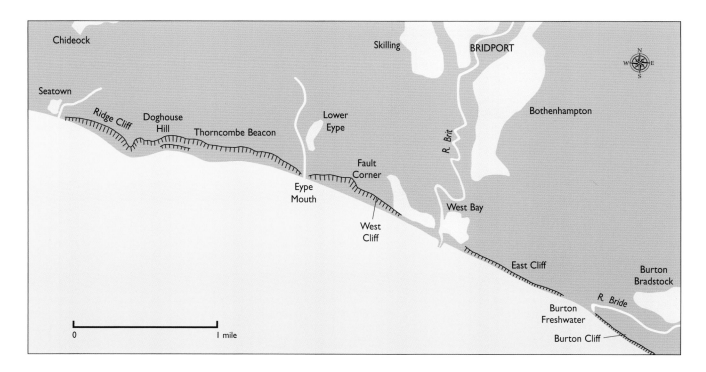

in the shadow of East Cliff at West Bay, begins the great sweep of Chesil Beach that runs unbroken for 18 miles to the Isle of Portland to the south-east. Although the varied colours and profiles of the cliffs contribute most to the character of this stretch of coast, the gaps cut by streams at Eype, West Bay and Burton Freshwater not only give access to the shore but also have encouraged man's activities along what would otherwise be an inhospitable coastline. Each break in the coastline is different; at Eype the little stream has cut a steep-sided valley that has not allowed development at the coast, with Eype village nestling at a safe distance inland;

at West Bay, the valley and estuary of the Brit have led to the growth of harbour, resort and retirement homes; and at Burton Freshwater, the caravan park shelters, perhaps a little uneasily, behind the shingle of Chesil Bank's western extremity. So between Seatown and Burton Bradstock there lies a coast of contrasts. High cliffs, remote in the west, alternate with busy summer beaches. When the dead hand of winter has brought some quiet to both resort and caravan park, Channel storms lash cliff and beach alike, bringing inevitable, and often irreversible change to this coast.

West Bay from the top of East Cliff

Once again, geology is largely responsible for the variety that is encountered along the cliffs of this coastline. Geologically speaking, it is a coastline of two halves; to the west of West Bay, the cliff faces display a wide variety of rocks from summit to beach level, while to the east the same rock type, yellow Bridport Sands, dominates much of the cliff profiles, although they possess a thin limestone capping at the top. Between Seatown and Eype Mouth, clays and sands of Lower Jurassic age tend to dominate, although Thorncombe Beacon, like Golden Cap to the west, has a capping of younger Cretaceous rocks. The clay formations in these cliffs are unstable, and are largely responsible for the land-slipping that occurs, with the now-familiar boulder arcs at the foot of Thorncombe Beacon marking the extent of former slips. Between Eype Mouth and West Bay lies Fault Corner, where a major fracture in the rocks has brought Lower Jurassic rocks into contact with younger rocks of Mid-Jurassic age. All of the cliffs in this short stretch of coast are very unstable, and the beach is littered with tumbled masses of rock that have fallen from their higher slopes.

East of West Bay, the cliffs possess one of the most distinctive profiles anywhere along the Dorset coast. Within the yellow Bridport Sands are some bands that are more resistant to erosion than others, and these tough layers protrude to give the cliffs their characteristic serrated appearance. At Burton Freshwater there is a break in the long cliff wall where the little River Bride reaches the sea. Its waters are, however, dammed back by the shingle of Chesil Beach and only reach the sea by seepage through the pebble bank. Occasionally, when the Bride floods, the river will burst through the shingle, cutting a deep gap, which may persist for days or even weeks. Eventually shingle is drifted back across the river's exit and the long sweep of Chesil Beach is restored.

Beyond Burton Freshwater, Burton Cliff presents another almost-vertical profile, but it is eroding rapidly enough for

The coast of Lyme Bay, looking east from Thorncombe Beacon

The coast looking west from Eype Mouth, with Thorncombe Beacon and Doghouse Hill

the coastal path along the top to have been moved back for safety reasons. Eastwards of the National Trust car park at Burton Bradstock, the character of the coast changes again; the Bridport Sands are replaced by clays, which once again give rise to landslipping. At the appropriately named Cliff End, the low cliffs give way to the shingle of Cogden Beach and the majestic curve of Chesil running away to distant Portland.

Burton Cliff, east of Burton Bradstock

West Bay: coastal defences and rough sea

Although landslipping and erosion are a problem along much of this coast, they have caused the greatest concern at West Bay. Not only has the small resort and fishing settlement had to cope with these problems, but it has also suffered flooding during winter storms, when the sea has broken over the protective barriers of East Beach. Matters have been exacerbated by the removal of shingle from East Beach by the gravel industry over hundreds of years, although this ceased in 1983 after a public enquiry. Natural processes, however, seem to be continuing the work of man, for East Beach has seen a steady loss of material in the 1990s. West of the harbour entrance the local authority has had to fight a long battle against erosion and landslipping. The extension of the Esplanade westwards, the addition of rock armour on the seaward side, and the building of rock bastions have all been used to stiffen the defences. On the landward side of the Esplanade regrading

and drainage of the cliff have sought to produce stability and to protect the cliff-top buildings. Now an ambitious new scheme envisages a total reappraisal of the West Bay water-front, with a replacement West Pier, with rock armour protection on the seaward side, beach replenishment on West Beach and a rock armour groyne to protect West Beach.

In some ways West Bay and its problems represent something of an intrusion into this coast of colourful, eroding cliffs and shingle beaches. The building of the harbour walls in the mid-nineteenth century has caused a permanent disruption to the longshore movement of shingle, and to the long-term stability of the coastline. Seen from the summit of Golden Cap on a day of sunshine and clouds, it is the intermittent glow of the golds and yellows of the cliffs, that catches the eye; man's intervention may have brought unwanted change, but the coast's intrinsic beauty will survive.

6
CHESIL BEACH

This magnificent shingle structure, which extends for 18 miles from West Bay south-eastwards to Chiswell, nestling under the northern heights of Portland, is unique in Britain. For 8 miles of its length, it is bounded on the landward side by the Fleet, a tidal lagoon, which stretches from Abbotsbury to Small Mouth, just south of Wyke Regis, where it is linked to the open water of Portland Harbour. Frederick Treves, Dorset writer and Royal Physician, wrote of the beach:

No sea rampart can surpass it in bluster, in massiveness, in truculence. It stands alone defying the tide… In a westerly gale it is a place terrible to behold… the beach is torn at by the receding waves as if the straitened foam were a myriad of claws.

John Trenchard, in J. Meade Falkner's *Moonfleet*, 'loved to see it best when it is lashed to madness in the autumn gale… and to hear the grinding roar and churn of the pebbles like a giant organ playing all the night.'

The great sweep of the beach is best appreciated from two viewpoints, from Verne Yeates at the northern end of the Isle of Portland, and from Abbotsbury Hill, high above the western end of the Fleet and Abbotsbury's Swannery. From Verne Yeates, Chesil Beach appears to emerge from the shadow of West Weare, and the breakers in Chesil Cove (Deadman's Bay in Thomas Hardy's *The Well-Beloved*) remind us of the power of the sea, and of the many shipwrecks that have occurred on this hostile coast. The shingle bank stretches away to the north-west, its seaward slopes broken by the sharp contours of ridges thrown up by past Channel storms. Its inland-facing flanks slope down more gently to the silent waters of the mysterious Fleet. Even on the clearest of days its western limits are not visible as

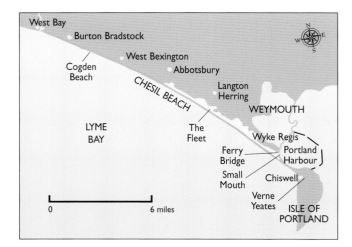

Chesil Beach from Verne Yeates

Chesil Beach, with Isle of Portland in the background

Moonfleet, seen from Chesil Beach across the Fleet

it merges imperceptibly with the blue hills and ridges leading to the coast of West Dorset. From Abbotsbury Hill there is a clearer view of the Fleet, edged with little promontories and bays on the landward side; the beach makes its lonely and majestic curve away to distant Portland, effectively linking the great detached block of limestone to the mainland.

Chesil Beach varies in both height and width from west to east. At Abbotsbury it is 22ft high, but at Chiswell it is a much more dominant feature, reaching almost to 50ft. At Burton Bradstock it is nearly 200ft wide, but at Wyke Regis the bank extends over 800ft from the breakers on Lyme Bay to the unruffled expanse of the Fleet. Most of the pebbles on the beach are of flint from the Chalk, chert (hard siliceous material similar to flint) from the Upper Greensand of West Dorset, limestone from Portland, and some 'foreign' rocks that have travelled from much farther afield in Devon and Cornwall. One of the most remarkable features of the beach is the way in which the pebbles vary in dimension from pea-size at West Bay to cobble-size at Chiswell. It is said that fishermen could tell where they were on the beach, when they came ashore, by the size of the pebbles, although recent research has shown that an even grading of pebbles from one end of the beach to the other does not exist in reality.

Researchers still seek an adequate explanation of the variation in the size of pebbles; current thinking suggests that once the thicker pebbles have been picked up by waves, they travel more easily than smaller ones, and thus show some concentration at the south-eastern end of the beach. Movement of pebbles along the beach seems to be from west to east as far as Wyke Regis, but at the Chiswell end the pattern of movement is much more variable.

The origin of Chesil Beach has exercised the scientific skills and ingenuity of researchers for a long time. Present opinion tends to favour the view that it came into being during the glacial period, when sea levels were much lower. Most of Lyme Bay would thus have been dry land, and rivers draining into the present bay would have deposited great aprons of gravel and sand material across the exposed sea floor. As the sea level began to rise in post-glacial times (as water was returned to the sea from the melting ice-caps) this spread of debris would have been swept up and driven landwards to occupy its present position. Much clay material and peat would have accumulated in an early version of the Fleet and the fact that such deposits have now been found to the seaward of the beach is ample evidence for its landward migration.

Managing Chesil Beach presents an enormous challenge to coastal engineers. It is at either end, where coastal settlements lie adjacent to the beach, at West Bay and at Chiswell, that the threat of flooding has led to a pressing need for management. The new coastal management scheme at West Bay was described in the previous chapter *(page 24)* so here the emphasis is on the flood protection scheme at Chiswell. The sturdy maritime community has hada long and troubled experience of flooding dating back to 1824, when 28 people were drowned and 80 houses damaged. Much of Chiswell lies well below the level of the beach and, until the recent scheme was completed, was under constant threat. Severe flooding in 1978 and 1979 made it clear that an integrated plan for flood management was essential for Chiswell and the A354 leading to Weymouth in the lee of Chesil Beach. The Esplanade wall was strengthened and new ramps and flood gates built into its structure. Gabion mattresses were put in place to raise the level of the beach crest to the north of the Cove House Inn. The most expensive part of the scheme was the construction of a new culvert which intercepts water percolating through the beach and discharges it into an open channel which has an outfall into Portland Harbour. Storms in 1989, 1990 and 1996 tested the new works to the limit, and they have proved to be extremely effective.

Chesil Beach at Chiswell

Chesil Beach from Abbotsbury Hill

Much of Chesil Beach is lonely and is visited only by enthusiastic fishermen at such places as Cogden Beach, West Bexington and near Ferry Bridge. The peace and solitude of the beach and the Fleet have done much to encourage a rich and varied bird population. At the western end of the Fleet is the famous Abbotsbury Swannery, which has existed since the fourteenth century, and elsewhere numerous bird species winter on the Fleet. Waders feed around the edges of the Fleet and the shingle itself is an important breeding ground for the common and little tern. In order to protect and sustain this bird population, much of the beach and the Fleet is a Nature Reserve. The Fleet management committee includes representatives from a number of interested and involved bodies, and the Fleet Study Group is dedicated to encouraging a wide range of research interests in the area.

To stand on the crest of Chesil Beach, under a sky of racing sunlit clouds and passing showers, when huge breakers are crashing onto the shingle, is to experience one of the finest seascapes in Britain. Nowhere is the majestic power of the sea more evident than along this shingle bank, exposed to waves generated in open water that stretches uninterrupted by land to South America. People have made little impact on the beach, and the empty loneliness of much of its length must remain its most precious asset.

7
THE ISLE OF PORTLAND

Seen from either the east or the west, the long sloping profile of the Isle of Portland is at once both unique and mysterious. Thomas Hardy called it 'the Gibraltar of Wessex' and Victor Hugo, in his novel *The Laughing Man*, wrote that:

The peninsula of Portland, viewed geometrically, presents the appearance of a bird's head, of which the bill is turned towards the ocean, the back of the head towards Weymouth; the isthmus is its neck.

Although the limestone block of the Isle of Portland is only 4.5 miles long and 1.75 miles wide, its coastline displays some of the finest cliff scenery in Dorset, if not along the whole of the south coast of England. Portland's steep limestone cliffs on its west coast, with the tumbled and chaotic screes at their base, face the full force of Atlantic storms and gales across the open waters of Lyme Bay. At Portland Bill

Winter storm at Chesil Cove

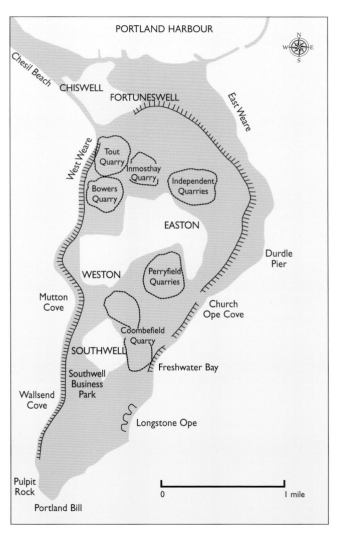

Fortuneswell and Chiswell

Mutton Cove

itself, where the sloping beds of limestone meet the disturbed, wave-flecked waters of the Race, Anne Garland, in Hardy's *The Trumpet-Major*, 'swept with her eyes the tremulous expanse of water around her that seemed to utter a ceaseless unintelligible incantation'. The east coast of Portland, although sheltered from the westerly winds that blow up the Channel, is exposed to strong easterly gales which stream across Weymouth Bay. Like parts of the west coast, the east is much affected by landslips, but the main cliffs of Portland limestone are more set back from the sea except to the south of Freshwater Bay. Frederick Treves found particular delight in the charm of Church Ope Cove: 'The glen is narrow and full of shade, a most gentle hollow in the cliffs opening to the sea.'

However dominant the physical landscape of the cliffs of Portland may be, the long occupation of the Isle by people has contributed much to the character of the coast. The working of Portland stone has scarred considerable lengths of the coastline, either through the opening of quarries in the cliffs, as at Freshwater and Longstone Ope in the south-east or through waste tipping from others slightly inland

such as Tout and Bowers in the north-west. The tightly packed underhill settlements of Chiswell and Fortuneswell add their own urban charm to the northern slopes of the Isle and the newly resurgent Portland Port maintains an important theme in waters rich in maritime history. The long defence associations of the Isle of Portland have left gaunt clusters of securely fenced buildings on the cliff top, and the three lighthouses add human interest to the bleak, windswept landscape of the extreme south.

In geological terms, the Isle of Portland is an immense block of limestone, sloping gently from north to south. Although limestone is the most distinctive element in the geology of Portland, it carries a cover of the Purbeck Beds over much of the Isle, and is underlain by two other formations; Portland Sand is immediately beneath, which in turn rests on Kimmeridge Clay. All of these rocks dip gently to the south, which means that in the north both Portland Sand and the much-obscured Kimmeridge Clay appear below Portland Limestone in the cliff sequence. However, in the extreme south the lower formations have disappeared below sea level, so that Portland Limestone forms all of the low cliffs.

As a result of the disposition of the rocks the coast is much affected by landslips, particularly in the north. It is only in the south-east, between Freshwater Bay and Portland Bill that landslips are absent. Some of the landslips, such as the one on which Chiswell is built, are now relatively stable and safe, but many are still active and potentially dangerous. Water easily percolates down through the joints (or vertical fractures) in the Portland Limestone, but cannot pass through the underlying clays, which become unstable and eventually founder, causing landslips to occur. The East Weare landslip in the north-east of the Isle, the second largest to be recorded in Britain, occurred in February 1792, and involved a strip of land 1.25 miles long slipping down nearly 50ft.

The form of the cliffs is largely a reflection of the landslipping process. In the north of the Isle, as at West Weare and East Weare, large sections of the cliff have slipped seawards, usually along a curved plane at some depth (known as rotational slipping). Along the east coast, near Southwell, great slices of the cliff have toppled seawards to form a particularly chaotic fringe to the coastline. Between

Church Ope Cove

Wallsend Cove and Mutton Cove on the west coast is one of the most impressive of Portland's cliffed coastlines. Here some sections of the cliff have toppled towards the sea again, but elsewhere the unstable and unsupported cliff has just sagged downwards.

In the extreme south of the Isle of Portland the famous raised beaches are exposed in the cliffs. To the west of Portland Bill lies the higher of the two beaches, capping the present cliff at a height of 50ft. It was probably formed about 210,000 years ago, when sea levels were higher during the warmer phases of the Ice Age. On the eastern side of the coast, just to the north-east of Portland Bill is the second raised beach, which lies 20–35ft above sea level; it is probably about 125,000 years old. It is much more easily accessible than the western one and remains of the shelly organisms that lived at that time can be clearly seen in the beach fragments.

The economy of the Isle of Portland has largely been based on the stone and defence industries. Rationalisation plans at the Ministry of Defence led to the closure of the Portland Naval Base in 1996, and the Royal Naval Air Station, HMS *Osprey* in 1999. These closures have obviously resulted in a large number of job losses, and over the last few years, Weymouth and Portland Borough Council have secured financial help from a number of sources in order to aid the restructuring of the economy. The Isle of Portland now has Assisted Area status, which allows local and incoming firms to obtain grant aid from the Department of Trade and Industry. Financial support has also become available from the European Konver 1 programme, designed to help defence-dependent areas diversify their economic base. Single Regeneration Budget funds are also available to assist in a whole range of initiatives such as tourism and environmental improvement.

The availability of this financial support has stimulated far-reaching economic change on the Isle of Portland. The area of the former naval base is now operated by Portland Port Ltd and companies already established there include Cable and Wireless and Inchcape Shipping Services. With such a varied and attractive hinterland it is possible that Portland Port will become an important cruise location. The Royal Naval Air Station is now being redeveloped as Osprey Quay with a sensible mix of land uses. Elsewhere the former Ministry of Defence establishment, situated high on the cliffs south of Weston, has become the home of the Southwell Business Park. The variety of businesses established there has already created 300 new jobs. Tourism also has an important role in the future of Portland. The natural scenic attractions of the Isle, combined with the wide range of opportunities available for activities such as climbing and diving around the coast, suggest that new visitor services, such as a new visitor centre at Portland Bill and a youth hostel at Castletown will lead to a significant growth in sustainable tourism.

The magnificent coast of the Isle of Portland has always been one of its special attractions and few will fail to be impressed by the awesome spectacle of great winter seas breaking over Pulpit Rock and its neighbouring cliffs. By way of contrast, Church Ope Cove on a fine summer day offers an almost Mediterranean-like ambience with its boulder-fringed beach, stark limestone cliffs, azure skies and sparkling sea. The human face of Portland is set for necessary change, but its massive physical landscape will provide an ever-present reminder of its fascinating Jurassic geology.

8
WYKE REGIS TO WHITE NOTHE

This stretch of the Dorset coast, which extends from the new suburban homes overlooking Portland Harbour to the commanding heights of White Nothe, offers a series of sharp contrasts in its physical and human landscapes. Much of the western part of this coast, from Wyke Regis to the eastern outskirts of Weymouth, is now built-up, although not without interest. The gaunt shell of the sixteenth-century Sandsfoot Castle, hugging the cliff just to the east of the cutting that carried the railway from Weymouth to Portland, reminds us of the long history of defence establishments along this coast. Further to the north-east is the sturdy, forbidding and well-preserved Victorian Nothe Fort, one of

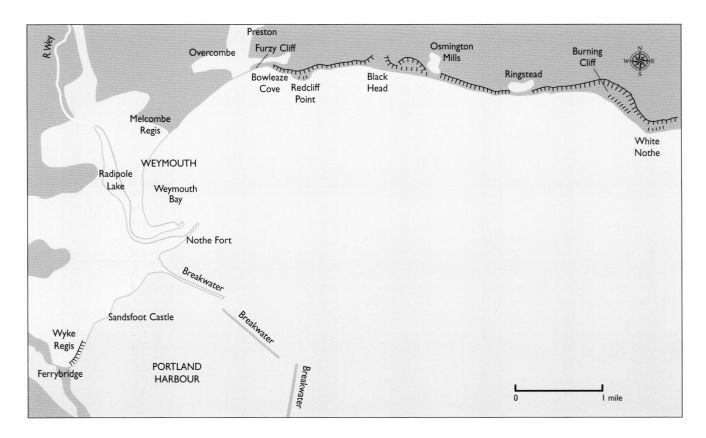

Georgian Terraces, Weymouth

Sandsfoot Castle

White Nothe from Ringstead

the famous Palmerston Follies that never saw the heat of battle. Beyond the ferry terminals lies the fine sand of Weymouth Beach, backed by the elegant architecture that Thomas Hardy thought, in his description of nineteenth-century Weymouth (his Budmouth) 'still retained sufficient afterglow from its Georgian gaiety to lend it an absorbing attractiveness'. Today's proliferation of seaside shops, fast-food premises and amusement arcades might cause some dissent, although the stylish sweep of Georgian terraces around the bay still provides a vista unique in southern England.

Beyond Melcombe Regis the coastline is different. The reed-fringed pools of Lodmoor Nature Reserve, with its outstandingly rich bird life, now lie secure behind the completed sea-defence works of Preston Beach Road. To the east Overcombe and Preston are the last outliers of suburban Weymouth, and beyond the holiday complexes of Bowleaze Cove, landslipped cliffs and shingle or boulder beaches suggest perhaps a theme recurring from West Dorset. However, the similarity is superficial, for here the rocks are different; they belong to the Upper Jurassic Period; the cliffs are much lower and the foreshore quite broken by the sharp ledges of Corallian rocks, particularly between Osmington Mills and Ringstead. Beyond is the great headland of White Nothe, which forms a magnificent backdrop to the whole of the coast east of Weymouth. Here the Chalk makes its most westerly appearance on the Dorset coast, forming white, flint-riven cliffs that fall some 550ft into the sea. The writer, Llewelyn Powys, who lived for six years in one of the coastguard cottages that cling to the summit of White Nothe, called it 'the noblest of all the Dorset headlands'. He spent much time exploring the undercliff, where 'it would take a boy longer than a summer's holiday to explore... the giddy ledges and castle rocks in that strip of broken ground.'

The coast from Bowleaze to White Nothe lacks the powerful drama of the huge sweep of the Chalk cliffs to the east or the overwhelming dominance of Thorncombe Beacon and Golden Cap in the cliffs of West Dorset. Nevertheless, it has its own intimate, almost secretive charm, for there is access only at Osmington Mills and Ringstead. The boulder-strewn beaches at Redcliff Point and the tumbled foreshore below White Nothe both have a deserted atmosphere, rare on the Dorset coast. Visitors find their way to the beaches below the villas and caravan park at Ringstead, or filter down from the Smugglers' Inn at Osmington Mills, but the long shingle stretches to the west and east seldom attract people apart from those staying at the adventure centre at Osmington Bay.

There is much geological variation along the coastline. Between Ferrybridge and the Nothe, the low, often overgrown cliffs are formed firstly of the Kimmeridge Clay, and further to the east, from Sandsfoot Castle onwards, of the Corallian Beds, which are also responsible for the higher ground on which Wyke Regis itself is built. The Corallian Beds are a series of grits, limestones and clays, and their varying resistance to erosion is reflected in the subtle variations in coastal landforms that are seen along this stretch. Grits form the cliffs on which Sandsfoot Castle and the Nothe Fort are built, and small coves such as Castle Cove to the east of the castle have been cut in the less resistant clays.

Ringstead Bay, from White Nothe

To the east of the wide sandy expanse in front of the Esplanade at Weymouth, and the new Preston Beach Road defences, Upper Jurassic rocks again form the coastline. To the east of Overcombe the shingle beach is backed by crumbling cliffs formed of Oxford Clay. From Bowleaze Cove onwards landslipping and mudflows are a common feature of a coastline whose geology is complicated by a number of minor folds and faults. Immediately beyond Bowleaze limestones, grits and clays give rise to a confused and tumbled series of cliffs as far as Redcliff Point, where a wedge of Oxford Clay is fringed by a series of untidy mudflows that spread out over the beach in a series of unstable lobes. After Black Head's landslips, which have here developed on the Kimmeridge Clay, the coast takes on a bolder aspect east of Osmington Mills, with the Corallian grits and limestones forming cliffs that fall steeply to boulder-strewn beaches with a series of ledges running out to sea. East of Ringstead the Kimmeridge-Clay bluffs rise up to Burning Cliff. It was here that spontaneous combustion of the bituminous shale broke out in 1826 and persisted for several years. The early geologists Buckland and De la Beche visited the area in 1829 and were fascinated by the 'small fumaroles that exhale bituminous and sulphurous vapours and some of which are lined with a thin sublimation of sulphur'. Just beyond, Holworth House is the final coastal landmark before White Nothe. The building nestles half-hidden by its surrounding trees and sits a little uneasily above the disintegrating cliff in the Portland and Purbeck Beds.

Although much changed since its days of Georgian elegance, Weymouth still retains the atmosphere of the quintessential English seaside resort. Its port function too has seen the winds of change, but its harbour frontage remains an attractive asset to the town, with Brewers' Quay, Nothe Fort and Nothe Gardens offering further variety for the visitor. It is to the east of Weymouth that coastal engineers have had to face the problems of managing physical processes that have threatened both infrastructure and property. For many years Preston Beach Road was liable to closure when seas topped the beach and threw shingle across the carriageway, effectively blocking coastal access to Weymouth from the east. Diversions inland via Littlemoor involved inevitable congestion at roundabouts and road junctions and caused many motorists to endure longer journeys to work in the Weymouth area. Between 1995 and 1996 the beach underwent replenishment, and a new sea wall, incorporating a cycle track was built. The works seem to have resisted the worst winter storms, with no closure of the Beach Road. However, problems of shingle drift remain, and still require a solution. To the east the western end of Furzy Cliff is now protected by a sea wall built in 1984, and previously vulnerable properties are no longer under threat. Ringstead, too, has had its problems. Here erosion and slipping have caused concern to caravan and villa owners alike. Beach replenishment, better cliff drainage and the building of a groyne were seen as the solution, although local geologists insisted that these works would cause irretrievable damage to a world-class exposure and increase erosion further to the east.

These shores of Weymouth Bay offer a felicitous mix of English seaside and Dorset's own rural charm. Seen from Llewelyn Powys' coastguard cottage on the lofty bastion of White Nothe, the graceful curves of Ringstead and Osmington Bays, fringed by small tangled copses through which tiny streams meander to the sea, seem a perfect contrast to the urban sprawl of distant Weymouth.

9
WHITE NOTHE TO MUPE BAY

The spectacular Chalk and limestone cliffs that form the coast between White Nothe in the west and Mupe Bay in the east display some of the finest scenery on Dorset's coast. Chalk forms the high precipitous cliffs between White Nothe and Durdle Door, as well as the high backdrop to Lulworth Cove, whilst Jurassic limestone cliffs line the coast from Dungy Head to Mupe Rocks. The diversity of the coast is further enhanced by the red, orange and yellow sands and clays that form the tumbled cliffs on either side of the little Durdle promontory, at the eastern end of St Oswald's Bay, along the eastern and western fringes of Lulworth Cove and in Mupe Bay itself. Frederick Treves found it a coastline of 'wide open bays, and fissured, sea-echoing chines' and 'round coves, inlets reached through arched rocks, level sands and moaning caves.'

At the western end of this stretch of coast there is a sense of unchallenged remoteness. Here the high sweep of the vertical Chalk cliffs from White Nothe to Bat's Head allows no access from the coastal path and its shingle and sand beaches are always deserted. On a bright summer's day the brilliant white of the cliffs and the azure blue of the pellucid

sea form a contrast of almost overwhelming intensity. Between Durdle Door and Lulworth Cove it is the amazing variety of coastal landforms that Treves so aptly described which command attention. These two features have acquired a status symbolic of the whole of the Dorset coast, and are studied universally as archetypal examples of coastal erosion.

Swyre Head and Bat's Head

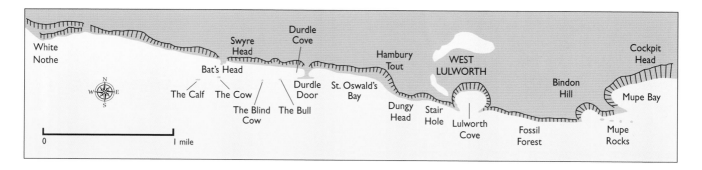

Lulworth Cove

From the heights of Hambury Tout, between Durdle Door and Lulworth, the view embraces a coastline whose intricacies of half-enclosed cove and open bay, of shingle foreshore and wave-flecked offshore rocks are unparalleled in southern England. It is not surprising that that this coast attracts millions of visitors each year, and that the most heavily used section of the entire South West Coast Path is that between Lulworth and Durdle Door. Beyond Lulworth to the east the scene changes again; this stretch is within the Lulworth Ranges and consequently is only accessible to the public at weekends and during the major holiday periods. Mupe Bay, like the high Chalk cliffs in the west, also has a feeling of remoteness for much of the year, although the peace and solitude is broken often enough by the alien sounds from the gunnery ranges on the landward side of Cockpit Head.

Geology has made a fundamental contribution to the dramatic scenery of this coast. Some twenty million years ago southern England's rocks dating from the Jurassic, Cretaceous and Tertiary periods were involved in huge earth movements in which the rocks were folded, compressed and uplifted. In South and East Dorset this resulted in the formation of two enormous structures, known as the Weymouth and Purbeck anticlines or upfolds. Millions of years of erosion have removed most of the rocks in these structures, but the northern limb of the Weymouth upfold, where the rocks dip steeply northwards (reflecting the great forces being exerted from the south) still remains in place along the coast from White Nothe to Mupe Bay. The different layers of rock are arranged parallel to the east-west coast and this disposition is basic to the development of the coastal scenery. Fronting the coast is the tough outer rampart of Portland Limestone. The Purbeck Beds (mainly limestones and shales, which are more prone to erosion) are immediately to the north on the landward side. The much wider outcrop of sand and clay (the Wealden Beds) is encountered next and, finally, to the north is the outcrop of Chalk.

Stair Hole, just to the west of Lulworth Cove, illustrates the earliest stage of the erosion of the outer Portland Limestone barrier. Aided by lines of weakness in the limestone, waves have cut a series of intricate caves and arches and have broken through into the Purbeck Beds on the landward side, exposing the famous upfold in the rocks known as the Lulworth Crumple. On the northern side of Stair Hole, the sands and clays of the Wealden Beds are subject to much landslipping, which feeds material onto the small shingle beach, where it is washed away by the waves. It was often thought that Stair Hole represented an early stage in the formation of Lulworth Cove, but this is no longer thought to be so. Erosion of the Portland barrier at Lulworth Cove was aided by the existence of a gap where the present tiny stream that enters the cove near the beach café once cut an exit through the Portland Limestone to a land area to the south long since eroded away by the sea. Rising sea levels in post-glacial times took advantage of this gap to break into the softer Wealden Beds behind, resulting in the erosion of Lulworth Cove to its present near-perfect curve. The tough Chalk at the head of the cove has resisted further erosion.

Remnants of the Portland barrier are seen as far west as the offshore rocks with unlikely bovine names, such as the Calf, and the Blind Cow. Durdle Door itself is a remnant of the Portland rampart, as are Man o' War Rocks to the east. Durdle Cove, Man o' War Cove, St Oswald's Bay and, far to the east, Mupe Bay, are all examples of the breaching of the Portland Limestone barrier and the subsequent erosion of the less resistant sands and clays of the Wealden Beds.

Two issues dominate the contemporary scene along the coast from White Nothe to Mupe Bay. Lulworth Cove is one of the great 'honey-pots' of the Dorset coast, and this brings with it a whole host of attendant problems. Further to the east is the continuing military presence in the Lulworth Ranges, which has engendered controversy for many decades. Summer crowds descend on Lulworth every year, but it exerts its attraction throughout the year, and fine

Durdle Door and Man o' War Cove from Swyre Head

winter weekends see its car parks still busy. In summer the car park copes with the many visitors and is often full; new environmental improvements here, such as the planting of shrubs for screening purposes, are to be welcomed. However, some consider the car park to be an eyesore in the magnificent landscape of sea coast and Chalk downland that is the essential Lulworth and such opinions extend to the caravan and camp-site at Durdle Door, although its conifer screen does mask its intrusive effect when seen from the east. The much-used path between Lulworth and Durdle Door has now been resurfaced so that it is both safer and more durable. The Heritage Centre is a new and welcome addition to the facilities at Lulworth and plays a vital role in providing a valued interpretive view of the origins and development of the coastal landscape.

Although the Lulworth Ranges have always seemed to be an unwelcome intrusion into the outstanding scenery of this coast, they have acquired a measure of acceptance in recent years. Since the Nugent Report was published in 1974, public access is now possible for limited periods and levels of management within the Ranges are unquestionably both sensitive and efficient; much has been done to preserve the scenic and ecological heritage of the area. Rare flora and wildlife survive well within the area and its high conservation status is universally recognised.

Few coastlines can better the stretch from White Nothe to Mupe Bay for sheer magnificence of scenery. Its essential appeal lies in the variety of its landforms, the stunning

St Oswald's Bay and the Durdle promontory, from Dungy Head

contrasts in colour afforded by the distinctive geology and the constantly changing aspect of the sea in Weymouth Bay. It offers, too, unique variations in scale from the intimate splendour of rock structure and wave erosion in Stair Hole to the great sweep of the Chalk cliffs from Bat's Head to White Nothe. Concern does exist that its millions of annual visitors will eventually damage, perhaps irreparably, the very landscape assets that have drawn them to Dorset. The aspirations of all those responsible for the management of this outstanding coastline must face the inevitable reconciliation of adequate visitor provision with effective landscape conservation.

10
MUPE BAY TO KIMMERIDGE

Since this stretch of the Dorset coast lies almost entirely within the Lulworth Ranges, it can claim that for much of the year, it is one of the most empty and lonely of the county's shores. Within its limits is displayed coastal scenery of the very highest quality, again of international importance for its geology, its coastal landforms and wildlife. Stunning variety of scenery is the key to its magical appeal. High and precipitous Chalk cliffs, much scarred by rockfalls, run from Mupe Bay to the northern end of Worbarrow Bay, broken only by the delightful little secretive cove at Arish Mell. Worbarrow Bay itself is backed by eroding, unstable and landslipped cliffs cut in the orange, brown and yellow sands and clays of the Wealden Beds. Beyond, Gad Cliff, with its distinct wedge-shaped profile, looks down on its tumbled undercliff, one of the most inaccessible and rarely visited places on the whole of the Dorset coast. Dark, fragile and flaky Kimmeridge Clay forms the coast of cliffs, benches and

Gad Cliff from the east

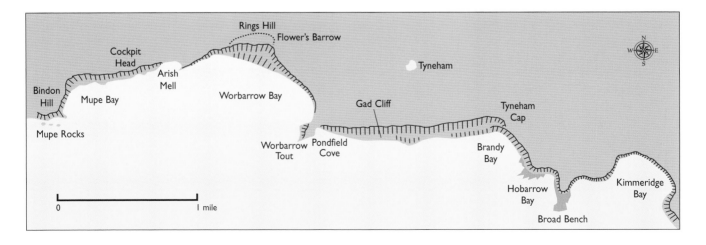

ledges as far as Kimmeridge Bay itself, rich in industrial archaeology and the site of Dorset's only Marine Nature Reserve. The occupation of this stretch of coast by the Ministry of Defence is still much lamented, but its stewardship has also brought undoubted benefits. Careful and sensitive management of its diverse natural habitats has given conservation a high profile throughout the Lulworth Ranges. Some of Britain's rarest plants survive here on Chalk and limestone cliffs and grasslands, which are also home to rare butterflies and great colonies of seabirds. The Range Walks, which include all of this section of the South West Coast Path, said by many to be the most strenuous of the whole trail, are open to the public most weekends and for the major holiday periods. Nevertheless Worbarrow Bay,

still intensely busy on fine summer weekends, has been spared the scars of seaside development that mar other parts of our coast. Seen on a winter's morning, when an easterly wind barely ruffles its sheltered waters, Worbarrow, with its pastel-shaded cliffs and silent shingle shore, is unparalleled in its tranquillity and loneliness. Here a very special coastal landscape has survived, despite being only 20 miles from Bournemouth, one of the largest conurbations on the south coast of England. A few miles to the east Kimmeridge Bay, despite its oil well, has continued to be a coastal niche of character, with its kilns, jetties and tramways long-since silent. Today its tidally exposed and seaweed-clad ledges are seaside fun for inquisitive children, while its deeper waters are leisure zones for surfers and sub-aqua divers.

Arish Mell and Cockpit Head

Kimmeridge Bay and Hen Cliff

Brandy Bay

The geological structures in this section are a continuation of those seen in the last section of the coast at Lulworth. The different rock groups run parallel to the coast; the oldest is the Kimmeridge Clay, of Upper Jurassic age, and the youngest is the Chalk, of Upper Cretaceous age. In the west of this stretch of coast, the Portland Limestone originally extended as a ridge from Mupe Rocks to Worbarrow Tout. However, there was probably a breach in the ridge where the little Arish Mell stream had, with its tributary the Tyneham stream, cut a gap similar to that eroded by the small stream at Lulworth. The rising post-glacial sea level would have broken into the lowland of the Wealden Beds that was once continuous between Tyneham and Mupe. The Wealden Beds, as along the Lulworth coast, offer little resistance to wave attack and were thus easily eroded to form Worbarrow Bay and Mupe Bay. At Arish Mell the tiny stream visible today was responsible for cutting the gap between Bindon Hill on the west, and the long slope up to Rings Hill on the east. Below Flower's Barrow, great masses of slipped Chalk and Greensand run down to Worbarrow Bay in a tumbled chaos of detached white, ochre and grey-green rocks and topsoil. Worbarrow's northern beaches seem more prone to change than most, with fresh falls of debris brought down each year to be eroded by the sea.

At the south-eastern end of the bay, Worbarrow Tout, with its own easily distinguished profile is really a continuation of Gad Cliff to the east, separated from it by the narrow neck of land leading down to Pondfield Cove. This low gap is of interest, and two origins are suggested for it. It is possible that the tiny Tyneham stream, that enters the sea at the southern end of Worbarrow Bay, may have originally turned through a right angle here and entered the sea in Pondfield Cove, or to the south of it. Alternatively, an even smaller stream flowing northwards from long-lost land to the south of Pondfield may have passed north through the gap to join the Tyneham stream.

Gad Cliff, with its huge overhanging profile, is one of the most dramatic features of this coast and its serrated cliffs, rising to the east can be seen from Portland Bill on a clear day; they dominate all views of this coast from as far east as St Aldhelm's Head. Beneath the vertical cliffs of Portland Limestone there is another undercliff of landslipped material – the result of the instability of the Kimmeridge Clay that underlies the length of Gad Cliff. Beyond, to the east, is the succession of bays cut in the shales of the Kimmeridge Clay, beautifully displayed for the walker who rests on the appropriately named Ocean Seat near Tyneham

Cap. Lonely Brandy Bay, Hobarrow Bay and Kimmeridge Bay are all backed by crumbling cliffs and fringed on the seaward side by stone ledges and rock platforms that are exposed at low tide. Erosion continually nibbles away at these rock masses leaving an untidy jumble of yellowing boulders on their seaward side.

Military acquisition of land in this area began as long ago as 1917, but it was in 1943 that Tyneham village and the surrounding area passed to the Ministry of Defence. All civilians were evacuated in December 1943 and an uninhabited silence fell on the village, its surrounding farms and the seaside cottages at Worbarrow. The words pinned to the church door as the last villagers left, 'Please treat the church and houses with care... we shall return one day and thank you for treating the village kindly' were poignant enough at the time, and have remained enduringly so. Apart from Kimmeridge at the eastern end, this coast remains empty and devoid of population and seems likely to remain so for the foreseeable future. The loss of Tyneham as a thriving village community must remain one of the most regrettable episodes in the history of Dorset's coast. On a happier note, however, the Nugent Report of 1974 led to the opening of the Range Walks, which enables walkers to enjoy the magnificent scenery of this coastline for most weekends of the year and in holiday times.

From the Iron Age fort of Flower's Barrow, crowning the Chalk heights above Worbarrow Bay, the unsurpassed views convey the very essence of this coastline. Westwards the eye can take in the great vertical Chalk heights of Cockpit Head, half-hidden Arish Mell and the distant mellow cliffs forming a tumbled backdrop to the sheltered waters of Mupe Bay. Immediately below lies the near-perfect curve of Worbarrow itself, with its southern, sheltering bastion of the Tout. Beyond, to the east, rises the long inland flank of Gad Cliff and the gap between this ridge and the beautifully shaped knoll of Tyneham Cap allows glimpses of the limestone cliffs of far-off St Aldehelm's Head. Whatever the future may hold for this western corner of Purbeck, its special heritage qualities will remain undiminished.

Worbarrow Bay, from Flower's Barrow

11
KIMMERIDGE TO DURLSTON HEAD

Stark contrasts abound along this coast of high cliffs, broken only where narrow valleys descend towards the sea. From Kimmeridge's ruined Clavell Tower vertical, dark shaly cliffs extend away unbroken towards the east until the little coastal waterfall at Freshwater Steps is reached. Beyond the lonely and seldom-visited Egmont Bight, the sheer physical presence of the menacing mass of Houns-tout, with its grey limestone capping, dominates the coastal scene. Across the half-enclosed waters of Chapman's Pool the long line of limestone cliffs of Emmetts Hill leads away to the shallow valley of Pier Bottom, left hanging halfway up the cliff above the slipped chaos of the lower slopes. Southwards lies the distinctive profile of St Aldhelm's Head, one of the great landmarks of Purbeck's coast. Stretching away to the east is another long expanse of cliffed coastline, cut entirely in the grey Portland Limestone, scarred by now-silent quarries and broken only where the valleys of Winspit and Seacombe

reach the sea. Anvil Point's lighthouse marks the end of these lonely wave-battered cliffs where Purbeck's bleak limestone plateau reaches the Channel. Beyond, Durlston Castle, nestling in dark, shady woodland conspicuously absent elsewhere along this coast, gives a first hint of the urban villas and stone terraces of resort and retirement Swanage.

This is another almost-deserted section of Dorset's coast, with farms, hamlets and villages set back in sheltered valleys or shallow hollows a mile or so inland. Two of the great country houses of Purbeck, Smedmore and Encombe, set within sheltering ornamental trees, have a distant glimpse of the sea beyond the windswept fields that run down to the crumbling cliffs east of Kimmeridge. Today man has little presence along the coast itself. Chapman's Pool has its small cluster of fishermen's huts, sheltered in the tangled undergrowth that runs down to the bouldery shore from the stony

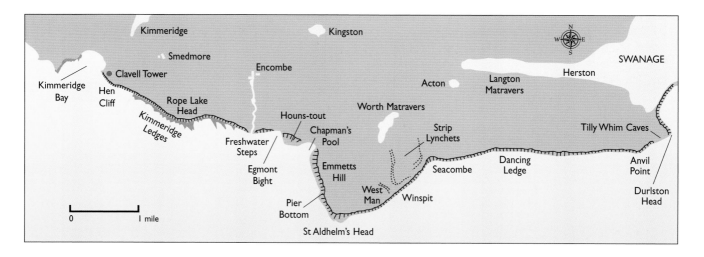

Winspit

Houns-tout from Emmetts Hill

heights of Emmetts Hill. St Aldhelm's Head proudly carries its chapel, its Coastwatch building and its white coastguard cottages on its bleak cliff top. Beyond the medieval strip lynchets that line the face of West Man, Winspit's quarries lie desolate and abandoned, their disused galleries contrasting darkly with sunlit cliffs on bright summer days. Seacombe repeats the scene on a smaller scale, and Tilly Whim's galleries have long since been closed for safety reasons.

This coast has tragic memories too. Purbeck's worst shipping disaster saw the *Halsewell* wrecked on the cliffs between Winspit and Seacombe with the loss of 168 lives in 1786. More recently the *Treveal* foundered on the Kimmeridge Ledges south-west from Egmont Point in 1920 and 36 crew were drowned in their ill-fated attempt to reach the shore.

The geology of this stretch of coastline is relatively simple. From Kimmeridge Bay eastwards the rocks dip gently to the south-east and thus beds outcropping in the cliffs become progressively younger in that direction. The intense folding in the Jurassic rocks, so well displayed in the rocks around Lulworth, is absent here and the strata are only disturbed by faults, many of which can be clearly seen in the cliff face. Kimmeridge Clay forms all of the cliffs from Hen Cliff at

the eastern end of Kimmeridge Bay as far as Egmont Bight. The thin shaly beds of the Kimmeridge Clay are susceptible to erosion and tend to crumble away readily so that in many places along these dark cliffs there is an almost-continuous fall of debris. The sequence of the shale beds is punctuated by the occurrence of much harder limestone bands, known as cementstones. These tough layers extend out to sea to form the notorious Kimmeridge Ledges, characterised by a line of breakers at low tide. Looking east from Rope Lake Head, roughly halfway between Kimmeridge and Freshwater Steps the cementstone bands can be clearly seen, dipping away eastwards until they descend to beach level. The Blackstone, worked as an oil shale in the past, also outcrops in the cliffs here and several old levels are still visible.

East of Freshwater Steps, where the tiny Encombe stream emerges from the wooded South Gwyle, the cliffs take on a new dimension. Houns-tout rises to over 500ft. Portland Limestone occurs at the top, eroded into weird castellated forms. Immediately below is the Portland Sand, which forms the vertical middle section of the cliff. The base of Houns-tout is formed of Kimmeridge Clay and is much slipped with boggy reed-filled hollows alternating with impenetrable thickets of blackthorn. The geological conditions here are very similar to those at the northern end of the Isle of Portland, with the Portland Beds overlying the Kimmeridge Clay – the ideal conditions for landslipping. Massive landslips have altered the face of Houns-tout on many occasions, destroying completely the old coastal road that led from Kingston to Encombe House. Arcs of boulders show where the landslips once extended into the sea, and narrowed the entrance to Chapman's Pool.

St Aldhelm's Head from below

Emmetts Hill, to the east of Chapman's Pool, is similarly affected by landslipping and, on occasions, slips have blocked the course of the small stream that drains down to the Pool, forming a small temporary lake.

Portland Limestone dominates the coastal scene all the way from St Aldhelm's Head to Durlston Head, since the Portland Sand and Kimmeridge Clay have now dipped below sea level. The limestone is a tough resistant rock and forms more or less vertical cliffs throughout this stretch. Faults occur in the limestone and in some places they bring up the softer Portland Sand, which is more easily eroded and causes overhangs in the cliffs. Overlying the Portland Stone are the Lower Purbeck Beds, which are generally less resistant and weather away to gentler slopes. They are much slumped in places and covered by rock debris resulting from frost action during the glacial period. Together the Purbeck and Portland Beds produce a distinct slope-and-wall profile along this coast. The dry valleys at Winspit, Seacombe and Anvil Point were all cut by running water and, after heavy winter rain, both the Winspit and Seacombe valleys carry a small stream for a while. All three valleys fail to reach sea level at the lower end of their courses and tend to hang some way up the cliff because when the valleys were occupied by streams, the latter were unable to cut down into the rock sufficiently quickly to keep pace with its erosion by the sea.

Quarrying has long since ceased along this limestone coast, with the last stone being extracted at Winspit shortly after the end of the Second World War. Portland Stone is, however, still produced from St Aldhelm's Quarry, only a short distance from the coast at the top of Pier Bottom. The building stones were worked from the upper part of the Portland Limestone sequence at Tilly Whim, Dancing Ledge, Seacombe, Winspit, St Aldhelm's Head and several other smaller quarries along this coast, and shipped away by sea. Human activity along this coastline is now essentially recreational, with climbing becoming increasingly popular on the cliffs at Anvil Point and on the disused quarry faces at Dancing Ledge and Winspit. The maintenance of the South West Coast Path is beset with problems on cliffs that are crumbling and slipping. At Chapman's Pool, the path now follows an inland diversion to Hill Bottom and new steps have much improved the steep ascents at Houns-tout and St Aldhelm's Head. Durlston Country Park provides a fitting end to this stretch of the Dorset coast, where walkers can enjoy well-managed natural habitats and visit an interesting interpretation centre.

Travelling eastwards from Lyme Regis, this section of the Dorset coast is the last empty and uninhabited stretch before the resort of Swanage, the crowded beaches of Studland and the conurbation of Bournemouth and Poole. Standing on St Aldhelm's Head the view westwards takes in all of Weymouth Bay and distant Portland, but closer at hand reveals the dark Kimmeridge Clay cliffs sweeping up through rich farmland to the dominant heights of Swyre Head and Houns-tout. Eastwards the contrasting limestone cliffs are just as wild and lonely and carry lasting memories of past shipwreck and busy quarry face.

The coast looking west from Dancing Ledge

12
DURLSTON HEAD TO SOUTH HAVEN POINT

Although not perhaps as spectacular as some stretches of coast to the west, this north–south section of Dorset's Purbeck coast offers some marked contrasts between Durlston's limestone headland and the low sandy shores at South Haven Point. The geological strata run at right angles to the coast and differential erosion has produced a series of bays separated by headlands. In the south is Durlston Bay, accessible only at the eastern end near Peveril Point and by the zigzag path that squeezes down to the shore in the centre of the bay. Its cliffs carry a woodland cover at the top in the south, half–hiding the grey bulk of Durlston Castle, but the trees give way firstly to the precariously perched blocks of flats and then to the open grassland of the Downs as Peveril Point is approached. Beyond the Point, which Hardy described in *The Hand of Ethelburta* as a 'sinister ledge of limestones, like a crocodile's teeth', lies the much more open expanse of Swanage Bay. Although much of the cliff top is now built over, it still offers the charm of a Victorian seaside resort. With its rolling backdrop of the eastern stretches of the Purbeck Hills, broken by the great gap at Ulwell, Swanage itself has an instant and unique appeal to both residents and visitors. The stone terraces and villas that climb steeply towards Durlston contrast well with the more open layout of the newer parts of the town that spread northwards towards the bungalows of New Swanage. To the north, where the Purbeck Hills meet the sea, they lose their smooth rounded outline and form the high Chalk cliffs that run from the tumbled landslips of Punfield Cove to Handfast Point and Old Harry and then westwards to South Beach, Studland. Low wooded cliffs form the coast as far north as Redend Point, with its slippery rocky foreshore of wave-eroded red and brown sandstones. Beyond lies Studland Bay, with its dune-fringed sandy shore, attracting thousands of

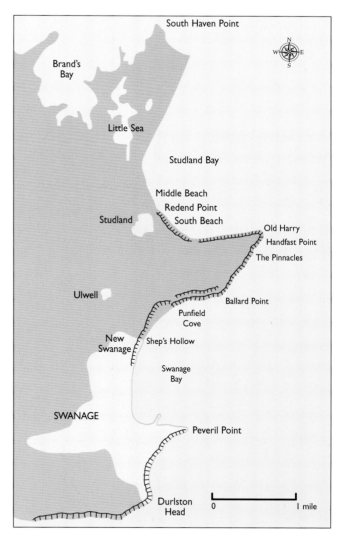

visitors on fine summer weekends, but offering welcome solitude on a grey winter's day when easterly winds send waves crashing onto the beach.

Durlston Bay is cut in the Purbeck Beds, where limestones alternate with shales and marls. Several of the beds are richly fossiliferous and have been an important collecting site for geologists for many years. The rocky ledges of Peveril Point include a coastal outcrop of the famous Purbeck Marble, not a true marble but a shelly limestone formed mainly of a tiny freshwater snail. Since the rock takes such a good polish it

was worked extensively at a number of inland sites and was widely used for decorative purposes in many churches, both locally and further afield, including Salisbury Cathedral. The wide sweep of Swanage Bay, like Worbarrow Bay, 10 miles to the west, is cut in the relatively non-resistant Wealden Beds. These are easily eroded by the sea and landslipping is a common occurrence on the cliffs, particularly in the unprotected section of the coast north of Shep's Hollow. Before the high Chalk cliffs are encountered beyond, the Greensands and the dark grey Gault make a brief appearance in Punfield Cove, with its high shingle beach and overgrown cliffs.

Durlston Bay

The coast near Shep's Hollow, Swanage Bay

Studland Dunes, with Old Harry in the distance

E.M. Forster was so impressed with the view from Ballard Down that he wrote, in *Howard's End*, that:

If one wanted to show a foreigner England, perhaps the wisest course would be to take him to the final section of the Purbeck Hills, and stand him on their summit… then system after system of our island would roll together under his feet.

In the cliffs beyond Ballard Point a feature unique in British geology, the spectacular Ballard Down Fault, is exposed. To the south of this curving fracture in the Chalk the beds are vertical, but to the north the beds dip and curve away to the north, so that they are almost horizontal at Old Harry Rocks. Erosion has worked away at the Chalk along this coast to produce scenery quite the equal of that between White Nothe and Bat's Head. The Pinnacles are huge stacks of Chalk, isolated from the cliffs by wave attack. To the north is the amazing erosional complex of Handfast Point and Old Harry. Hilaire Belloc wrote in 1925:

Old Harry is an isolated chimney of Chalk rock, which still stands expecting doom. He had a wife standing by him for centuries, a lesser (but no doubt nobler) pillar. She crashed some years ago and now he is alone.

The Dorset and East Devon World Heritage Site ends at the southern end of South Beach, Studland.

Studland Bay's dune shoreline is one of the few parts of the Dorset coast where deposition is causing seaward growth of the land. Over the last four hundred years records indicate a steady accumulation of sand dunes that have now isolated Little Sea as an inland body of water. However, erosion is now a serious problem on Middle Beach, Studland and sand removed from the old dunes here appears to drift north along the coast. Elsewhere the dunes still appear to be growing, although it has been suggested that they will develop less slowly than in the past.

Along such a widely varied stretch of coast, management issues are bound to vary. Erosion and cliff instability in Durlston Bay have caused much concern in recent years, resulting in the construction of the huge stone apron to protect the cliff-top flats. This has had a somewhat disfiguring effect on what are naturally attractive cliffs and raises the issue of the the effectiveness of land-use planning in sensitive sites. Swanage Bay has its share of erosional problems too, particularly beyond Shore Road, where there is much evidence of cliff instability. Beyond the sea wall, damage to

Old Harry and Handfast Point

the protecting wooden groynes means that the cliffs are becoming increasingly vulnerable to attack. The Swanage waterfront underwent inevitable change in the last two decades of the twentieth century. Although plans for a marina were abandoned in the late 1980s, the new Catalan-style flats near Peveril Point have added a modern element to the traditional seaside architecture. The outfall jetty in the centre of the bay, completed in 1993, has now become a familiar feature, although there is evidence that sand accumulating to the south of it is failing to reach the beaches to the north. Although recreational zoning for the whole of the bay was rejected, the proposed bathing-only sector is to be welcomed on safety grounds.

Since the National Trust became responsible for the management of the Studland shoreline, its appearance has been transformed. With such huge numbers of visitors in the summer, the provision of high-quality facilities is essential, and well-managed car parks, cafés, shops and information centres have done much to improve the situation.

Studland is also one of the most popular and widely used locations for field studies in Dorset, and the new eco-friendly education centre is another welcome addition. Management of the dune ecosystem and the adjacent heathland is also the responsibility of the National Trust, and carefully phased restoration projects should maintain the high conservation status that such precious natural assets require.

The sandy bays and high Chalk cliffs of Purbeck's eastern coast combine to present some of the Dorset coast's most attractive scenery. However, visitor pressure increases every year; Swanage is perhaps no longer recognisable as Hardy's Knollsea, 'a seaside village lying snug between two headlands', and Paul Theroux's 1982 description of Studland Bay as 'an empty mile of sand dunes and scrub' belies its summer popularity. The great challenge for the first few decades of the new century is indeed, in the words of the 1995 Strategy Document, to 'keep Purbeck special', and to seize the management opportunities that will ensure its continuing appeal.

13
POOLE HARBOUR

Poole Harbour, with its 60-mile coastline and occupying some 10,000 acres, is one of the Dorset coast's finest assets. It is an island-studded estuary, into which drain the waters of the Frome and Piddle rivers in the west and the shorter rivers from Purbeck's heathland in the south. The Sherford river drains into Lytchett Bay and several small urban streams of Poole empty into Holes Bay. Frederick Treves captured its estuarine ambience perfectly when he wrote of its 'maze of waterways, of capes and creeks, of islands and shoals, of gleaming water that here scoops a bay out of heather-tinted sands and there flickers like a light between the trunks of a clump of pines'.

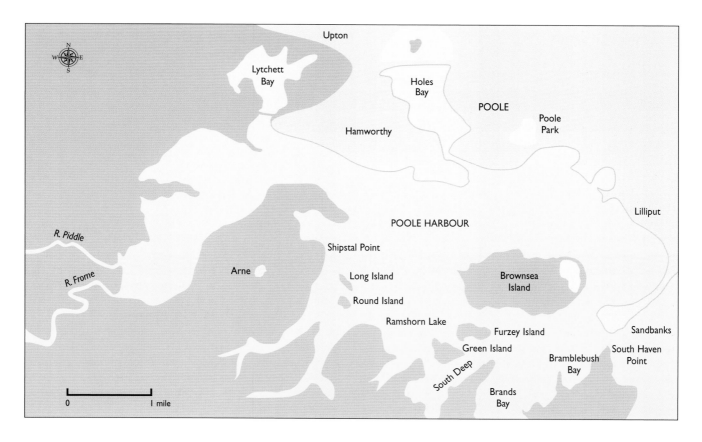

Long Island and Round Island, Poole Harbour

It is perhaps the overwhelming contrast between its northern and southern shores that defines its character most closely. Its northern shores are intensely urban, its southern shore deeply rural. The urban shores of Poole, Hamworthy and Lilliput have little uniformity of atmosphere. Hamworthy's shores are part holiday park at Rockley Sands, part housing estate and busy cross-Channel ferry port. Poole Quay still has the sturdy, confident outlook born of a long and distinguished maritime history, while the waterside villas and estates of Parkstone and Lilliput reflect the relaxed and easy atmosphere of retirement and recreation. The long sandy prow of Sandbanks half turns towards Poole Harbour, with its landing stages and pontoons and half turns away towards Poole Bay, with its groyne-protected beaches. The solitude and serenity of Poole Harbour's Purbeck shores belong to another, more remote Dorset. Here long twisting creeks, with mud-flats glistening at low tide, bear names that immediately capture the imagination – Middlebere Lake, Brand's Bay, Bramblebush Bay. Between the creeks, long salt-marsh-fringed tongues of land carrying heath and farm pastures, long since reclaimed from Purbeck's share of Egdon, as well as dark coniferous plantations, push out self-consciously towards the waters of South Deep and Ramshorn Lake. Intrusively, man has busied himself along these southern shores, exploiting the near-surface ball-clay deposits as well as exploring for and developing the deep-seated oil resources of Wytch Farm in the latter half of the twentieth century. Goathorn's piers may have echoed to the rumble of narrow-gauge trains delivering ball clay, but in the environmentally conscious present, BP's activities in the oilfield have been disguised and hidden with masterly care and scrupulous concern.

It is the islands of Poole Harbour that add further interest, and define its character more sharply. Brownsea, the largest of the islands, is inevitably the most well-known, particularly to the thousands of cross-Channel passengers who slip by its northern shores in the huge ferry vessels. In 1978 Jack Battrick, who was born and lived on Brownsea, wrote of the 'cliffs adorned with a thick growth of golden gorse, bell heather, and masses of bracken with the lofty Scotch and pine firs towering behind them.' Celia Fiennes, who visited the island in the late-seventeenth century was much impressed with the copperas works, which yielded liquids used in dyeing, tanning and ink making. Later, in 1907, Baden-Powell brought the island universal recognition with the famous camp that led to the founding of the Boy Scout movement. The other islands in the harbour are altogether more secretive. Furzey, with its its attractive house, has been the unlikely site of two oil wells, although BP is now considering its future development. The smaller islands, Green, Long and Round have had a variety of owners and possess an elusive charm born of remoteness and watery isolation.

Inevitably, geology plays a subdued role in the low cliffs, muddy creeks and sandy bays around Poole Harbour, compared to its dominant influence in the dramatic coastal landscapes of Purbeck, Portland and West Dorset. Poole Harbour is everywhere surrounded by rocks of the Poole Formation, which are principally sands and clays, well seen in the cliffs along South Shore, Brownsea Island and at Shipstal Point on the eastern side of the Arne Peninsula. Poole Harbour owes its origin to the climate getting warmer towards the end of the Ice Age; the extended ice sheets

Brand's Bay

Saltmarsh, Arne Bay, Poole Harbour

The Barfleur, *entering Poole Harbour*

started to melt, causing the sea level to rise. Before this much of the area of the present Poole Harbour was probably very similar to the lower-lying parts of Purbeck's heath – low sandy knolls separated by shallow depressions drained by streams that fed into the open valley of the main river, the Frome. The knolls were in places capped by a discontinuous sheet of gravel, deposited by the Frome and its tributaries when they flowed at a higher level in the earliest stages of the Ice Age. As the sea level began to rise after the Ice Age water flooded into the low-lying valleys of the Frome and its tributaries, drowning the lowest parts. The very highest parts survived as the islands within Poole Harbour, with the plateau summits of Brownsea still carrying the spreads of gravel laid down by the early equivalent of the present-day Frome. With the rising sea level the Frome and its tributaries were forced to adjust their courses and began to deposit thick spreads of silty material in their lower valleys, as well as in the newly formed waters of Poole Harbour. Thus many of the lower parts of the valleys draining into Poole Harbour are marshy and ill-drained, the result of this deposition. The extensive mud-flats exposed at low tide remind us that the depositional process is continuing and that Poole Harbour is slowly silting up – a process that is much nearer completion in enclosed areas such as Lytchett Bay and Holes Bay.

With a bird population of international importance, Poole Harbour has become a major site for nature conservation. The mud-flats exposed at low tide are feeding grounds for the large populations of waders and wildfowl and the salt marshes around the edges of the harbour are important nesting grounds; terns and gulls nest on the islands. Much of the harbour is now protected as a Site of Special Scientific Interest and under a European directive it is a proposed Special Protection Area for Birds and a proposed Wetland of International Importance under the Ramsar Convention.

Poole Harbour is also an extremely important location for a whole range of recreational water sports. Additionally, its commercial importance has grown steadily in the second half of the twentieth century, particularly with the growth of the cross-Channel ferry traffic, the growing trade in steel imports and the continuing export of ball clay. Clearly some overall management plan was necessary that would reconcile all the requirements of the conflicting activities within the harbour. Thus in 1994 the Aquatic Management Plan was launched as a means of balancing the fundamental conflicts which existed. The main thrust of the plan was to establish clear zoning of high-speed water-sports' activities, and to create a bye-law restricting powercraft to a speed of 10 knots throughout most of the harbour. Most of the Purbeck shore is clearly defined as a quiet zone.

So Poole Harbour remains an estuary of contrasting shores and waters that see a potential conflict of conservation, recreation and commerce. When Treves wrote in 1906, 'Go back ten centuries and this Wessex estuary is still the same as when up the fairway came the long boats of the Danes', he could not have foreseen the growth of the cross-Channel ferry port, or the proliferation of modern water sports. Even the tranquil Purbeck shore has seen the intrusion of clay workers and oilmen, although in latter years the exploitation of resources has been exceptionally well managed. An imaginative management plan is establishing sensible balance between its commercial growth, its recreational activities and its highly merited conservation status.

14
SANDBANKS TO HENGISTBURY HEAD: DORSET'S URBAN COAST

This is the stretch of Dorset's coastline that has probably undergone the most dramatic change over the last two hundred years. Before Lewis Tregonwell built his house overlooking the tiny Bourne stream in 1810, virtually all of this coast was uninhabited. Across the broad gravel terraces over which present-day Bournemouth sprawls, heathland, broken by pine copses, extended to a coast of yellow-and-buff-coloured cliffs, edged with a wide stretch of gloriously empty golden sands. Today, after two centuries of virtually continuous development, the 10 miles from Sandbanks to the last houses before Hengistbury's open spaces are an almost completely urbanised and managed coastline. As cliff-top houses, villas and hotels began to spread both eastwards and

westwards from the early settlement at the mouth of the Bourne, the twin needs for the protection of the rapidly eroding cliffs, and the provision of amenities for both residents and the ever-increasing number of visitors led to the building of sea walls and promenades from 1907 onwards. By 1975 the whole frontage from Poole Head to Solent Road at the eastern end of Southbourne was protected and the change was virtually complete.

To the east, Hengistbury Head, rich in archaeological remains from early-British (Stone Age to Iron Age) and Romano-British times, remains wild and untouched by permanent settlement. Its airy heights and open spaces are protected as

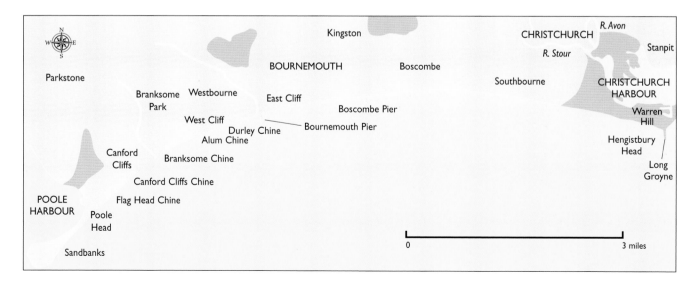

Canford Cliffs Chine

East Cliff, Bournemouth

Sandy cliffs between Poole and Bournemouth

a Local Nature Reserve and its archaeological sites are a scheduled ancient monument. It is from Warren Hill, Hengistbury's small gravelly summit plateau that Bournemouth and Poole's urbanised shoreline is best appreciated. To the west are the green open spaces of Whitepits and West Field, fringed on the seaward side by small cliff-top dunes. Beyond, the urban spread of Southbourne's residential areas leads away to the white high-rise blocks on both East Cliff and West Cliff in Bournemouth, which contrast sharply with the pine-clad cliff tops of Branksome and Canford Cliffs in the distance. The peninsula of Sandbanks, an unlikely mix of pines, villas and hotels, points away to the dune-fringed shoreline of Studland Bay and the distinctive blue outline of the surging Purbeck Hills that form the magnificent backdrop to one of southern England's finest urban shorelines. In *Tess of the d'Urbervilles*, Thomas Hardy called his Sandbourne a 'Mediterranean lounging place on the English Channel' and noted that:

> *… an outlying eastern tract of the enormous Egdon Waste was close at hand, yet on the very verge of that tawny piece of antiquity such a glittering novelty as this pleasure city had chosen to spring up.*

Over a hundred years later, this description still remains entirely appropriate!

It is along this stretch of coast, from Sandbanks to Hengistbury Head, that geology, not perhaps unsurprisingly, plays its most subdued role. For much of the distance between Poole Head and Solent Road, the cliffs are vegetated. In some places this vegetation is natural, as at Canford Cliffs where purple heather in bloom is an attractive summer adornment. However, much of the cliff frontage is planted with shrubs and bushes as part of a stabilisation policy. The cliffs of Poole Bay are composed of sands and clays of Tertiary age, capped over much of their length by Quaternary gravels, probably laid down by the ancient Solent River, when it was flowing at a higher level than that of the present sea level.

The most important event in the evolution of the shoreline of Poole Bay was probably the breaching by the sea of the Chalk ridge between the Isle of Wight and Purbeck, and the subsequent flooding of the lowland of the Solent River valley to the north of it, as post-glacial sea levels rose. Once the sea had broken through the ridge it found the sands and clays of the Solent River valley easy to erode and thus the present Poole Bay began to take shape. The flooding also extended into the part of the Solent River valley now occupied by Poole Harbour and the parts of the lower Avon and Stour valleys where Christchurch Harbour now exists. Along the northern edge of the newly formed Poole Bay the Tertiary sands and clays were easily eroded and formed cliffs, some over 100ft high, similar to those of today. Eroded material from the cliffs formed sandy beaches, although drift of some of this material along the shore led to the formation of the sandspits at Sandbanks and further east at Mudeford. Unusually, there is a change in the direction of this longshore drift at Durley Chine. To the west drift varies between south-west and north-east, yet to the east drift is predominantly towards the east.

Hengistbury Head, in common with the rest of this coast, erodes rapidly and the removal of the protective ironstone doggers from the foot of the cliffs in the nineteenth century for use in the iron furnaces of South Wales only exacerbated the problem. The Long Groyne was constructed in 1937–39 in order to arrest the movement of sand and shingle around the headland and allow the build-up of beaches in front of the cliffs, thus giving some measure of protection against erosion. Although the beaches did indeed build up in this spot, the loss of material drifting round the extremity meant that the cliffs beyond lost the renewing sand and shingle for their protective apron of beaches and themselves began to erode rapidly. Beyond, Mudeford sandspit also lost its supply of sand and suffered similar problems. Much of the coastal defence work here in the last half of the twentieth century has been devoted to solving the problems unwittingly caused by the building of the Long Groyne!

The construction of the sea walls and promenades along the sea front of Poole Bay, together with the various cliff-stabilisation schemes have afforded protection and provided an essential and much-valued amenity for both residents and

Earth Pillar, Warren Hill, Hengistbury Head

Bournemouth Pier

the sea walls and promenades along Poole Bay, change in the built landscape has transformed the appearance of Bournemouth's sea front. Few would recognise the approaches to Bournemouth Pier from mid-twentieth century times. The Pier Approach Baths are gone and the complex is now dominated by the red-brick International Centre, the Oceanarium, the elevated flyover and a state-of-the-art multiplex cinema. On either side both East and West Cliff have seen the proliferation of high-rise hotels and blocks of apartments – features that can be seen from the heights of far-off Cranborne Chase on a fine day. Boscombe's pier approaches are now being swept by the winds of change, with the construction of huge blocks of luxury flats that dominate the cliff tops to the east.

visitors. However, as with most coastal engineering, problems have arisen. The sandy beaches are one of the most prized assets of both Bournemouth and Poole, derived in the first instance from the erosion of the sandy material in the cliffs, but once the cliffs had been stabilised and sea walls and promenades built, an essential link in the coastal process system was broken since the principal source of the sand was no longer available. Thus in recent years, beach replenishment has become an essential element in the coastal strategy of Bournemouth Borough Council. Sand has been dredged from a number of locations offshore and pumped ashore along different stretches of the coast. The programme was first introduced in 1970 and is an ongoing operation with the next replenishment due in 2003–04.

Change inevitably remains a constant theme along the coast. If physical change has been subdued since the completion of

However, if seaside change is inevitable then certain elements of continuity also prevail. The cliff lifts still make their ungainly passage from cliff top to promenade, the wooded chines still provide relief and seclusion, and the elegant Russell Cotes Museum continues to offer the nostalgia of the past. The shores of Poole Bay are home to nearly half a million people, yet they seem to carry their urban burden lightly. Their cliffs, although they carry the essential elements of the modern seaside resort, retain pine trees and green open spaces along their tops, together with flashes of their original golden colour in places where vegetation is missing. If the shoreline possesses a certain elegance and charm, it is enhanced by one of the finest distant prospects in all of southern Britain. From any cliff-top viewpoint it is the twin Chalk headlands of western Wight and the Isle of Purbeck that draw the eye and complete the magnificent setting for Dorset's premier resort.

15
CHRISTCHURCH HARBOUR TO CHEWTON BUNNY

Dorset's far-eastern coast has little affinity with the other magnificently varied stretches to the west, save perhaps for some broad similarities with Poole Bay. Christchurch Bay, extending from Hengistbury Head to the extremity of Hurst Castle Spit in Hampshire, possesses some physical characteristics in common with Poole Bay, but does not share the intensity of its urban development. Christchurch Harbour, much smaller than Poole Harbour, has neither the commercial development nor the intricate nature of Poole Harbour's many hidden creeks and inlets. Nevertheless, standing on Hengistbury's Warren Hill, Christchurch Harbour, with the grey stone Priory at its head, the estuarine charm of the eastern waterside villages of Stanpit and Mudeford, the brooding presence of pine-covered St Catherines's Hill to the north, and the far horizons of Cranborne Chase and the New Forest in the distance, has an instant appeal.

Between Mudeford Quay and the Hampshire border at Chewton Bunny, the few miles of Dorset coast are part

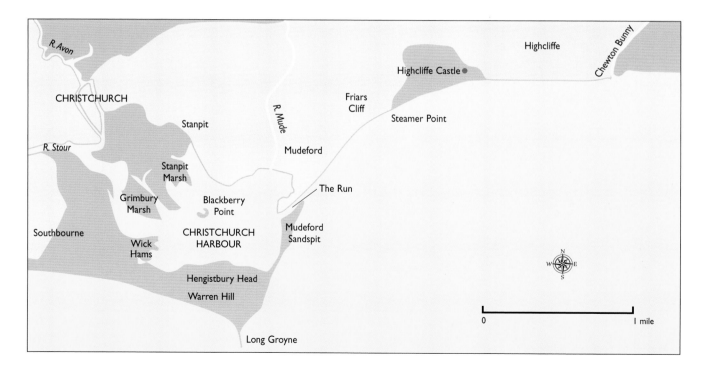

resort, as at Avon Beach, and part retirement shore at Friar's Cliff and Highcliffe. Here the cliffs are low; they are protected by a bare, curvilinear sea wall at Friar's Cliff, exposed and crumbling in front of Highcliffe Castle and totally managed at Highcliffe in a complex of terraces, drains and groynes that has a sad air of complete, if necessary, artificiality about it. Beyond the trickling stream of Chewton Bunny, the Hampshire coast to the east is a complete contrast, for here it is as yet untamed and its chaos of landslips and receding cliffs perhaps echoes some memories of the far west of Dorset, although it lacks Black Ven's threatening splendour.

Christchurch Harbour, in the lee of Hengistbury Head, owes its origin to the post-glacial rise in sea level. After the sea broke through the Chalk ridge between the Isle of Wight and Purbeck it flooded into the lowland drained by the ancient Solent River forming Poole and Christchurch Bays. Further flooding saw the drowning of the lower parts of the combined valley of the Avon and Stour rivers to form Christchurch Harbour. Today the two rivers flow into the harbour just south of the little promontory on which Christchurch Priory stands. Sediment brought down by the two rivers is gradually leading to the silting up of the harbour. It is fringed by large areas of salt marsh; in the

The Run and Christchurch Harbour

north lies the expanse of Stanpit and Grimbury Marshes, now largely drained and converted into grazing marsh, and along the leeward side of Hengistbury Head are the smaller salt-marsh areas at Wick Hams and surrounding Holloway's Dock close to Mudeford Sandspit. Although some parts of Grimbury Marsh are protected by a dyke, parts of the exposed fringe of Stanpit Marsh are now beginning to erode. Large mud-flats are exposed at low tide and are important feeding grounds for the internationally important bird life of the harbour.

On the seaward side of Christchurch Harbour is the notoriously unstable Mudeford Sandspit. When the iron-stone doggers were removed from the beach in front of Hengistbury Head in the mid-nineteenth century, eroded beach material was transported around the end of the headland and this led to unprecedented growth in the spit, so that by 1880 the end of the spit was opposite Highcliffe Castle. Growth of the spit has always been accompanied by later breaching of the structure near its root. The most recent breach took place in 1935, resulting in Highcliffe gaining a large beach from the remains of the northern end of the spit. In the second half of the twentieth century coastal defence work has focussed on bringing stability to the whole of the spit as well as to the other mobile feature of the coast here, the exit of the Stour and the Avon into Christchurch Harbour through the Run.

The low cliffs from Friars Cliff eastwards are firstly cut in sands, but at Highcliffe these give way to the infamous Barton Clay, responsible for landslipping both at Highcliffe and further east at Barton-on-Sea in Hampshire. Thus much of this cliffed coast is unstable and this has posed a threat to cliff-top properties. At Highcliffe this has resulted in extensive defence works being constructed from the 1970s onwards.

In a coastal environment that combines estuary, sandspit and low cliffs on the fringe of a huge urban area, management

Mudeford Sandspit

Mudeford Quay

Looking east along the Hampshire coast from Chewton Bunny

policies have to address a number of issues. The quiet waters of Christchurch Harbour, sheltered by Hengistbury Head, offer unrivalled opportunities for sailing and a whole range of other water sports. In common with other parts of the Dorset coast, conservation and recreation find themselves in uneasy opposition to one another. Christchurch Harbour displays a whole range of habitats, including salt marsh, mud-flats, reed beds and wet meadows, all of which support equally diverse plant and animal communities. In 1964 Stanpit Marsh, with its recorded 300 species of plants and 250 species of birds was designated a Local Nature Reserve. This gives some measure of protection to its outstanding bird life, which includes kingfishers and herons on its waterways, and a whole range of waders on the mud-flats of Stanpit Bight and Blackberry Point. Since 1986 the Site of Special Scientific Interest that covers the rest of Christchurch Harbour has been extended to include Stanpit Marsh.

Mudeford Sandspit carries an astonishing range of quite elaborate and well-built huts, chalets and cabins which house a substantial population during the summer months. Such investment in real estate demands some measure of protection in what is still an unstable physical environment. Coastal policy aims at stabilising the spit and since the middle of the twentieth century short sea walls have been built, new and more-substantial groynes added to hold the beach in place and beach-nourishment schemes put into operation. On the other side of the Run, Mudeford Quay and its sturdy historic buildings are protected from the swift currents at the mouth of Christchurch Harbour by steel piles. Beyond is a long concrete wall that protects tourist facilities at Gundimore. Avon Beach to the east is protected by sea walls and groynes, and further defences extend eastwards to Steamer Point. Some of these defences are now in poor condition and will need replacing. Highcliffe has seen a complete transformation of its sea frontage in the last thirty years. Cliff stabilisation, rock armour groynes and shingle nourishment of its beaches have brought much-needed protection. Along a coastline that has experienced so much instability and uncertainty in the past, there is still a sense of conflict between people and natural processes. Increasingly, coastal managers see the benefits of working with nature rather than against it. However, along a coast with such heavy investment in tourist and recreational facilities and in retirement homes, the costly expense of 'holding the line' must still be the policy envisaged for the foreseeable future.

Even in high summer, tranquillity and solitude are astonishingly easy to find around the shores of Christchurch Harbour. Stanpit's waterside, with colourful boats pulled up on the orange tide-washed gravel, looks serenely across to the long, low profile of Hengistbury Head and the visitor to Stanpit Marsh will often only have the lonely call of the curlew for company. Even the Hengistbury shore, with its toytown road train, salt marsh and patchy oak scrub, is still largely deserted. At the coast, on the sandspit, life in summer is perhaps busier, but still unhurried. It is in winter, when the grey waters of the Solent are flecked with foam along the Christchurch Ledge offshore and the distant Chalk hills of the Isle of Wight are half-hidden in mist, that this East Dorset shoreline reveals its true maritime character.